PROFITABLE FISHKEEPING

OTHER BOOKS AVAILABLE

Fancy Goldfish Culture 0 904558 - 63 - 0
    Frank W. Orme
Tobacco Culture — A DIY Guide 0 904558 - 28 - 2
    Guy N. Smith
Exhibition and Pet Mice 0 904558 - 25 - 8
    Tony Cooke, LRIC
Exhibition and Flying Pigeons 0 904558 - 27 - 4
    Harry G. Wheeler

This book is dedicated to Calvin Williams
in appreciation of much help in the past.

Plate 1.   Brown Trout.   (From a painting by Guy Dawson.)

PROFITABLE FISHKEEPING

by

GUY N. SMITH

With Coloured Illustrations by Jim Dunford

PUBLISHED BY SPUR PUBLICATIONS
SAIGA PUBLISHING CO. LTD
1 ROYAL PARADE, HINDHEAD,
SURREY, GU26 6TD, ENGLAND

Typeset by: Inforum Ltd, Portsmouth
Printed by: The Pitman Press, Bath

For the publishers:
SAIGA PUBLISHING CO. LTD
1 Royal Parade, Hindhead,
Surrey GU26 6TD, England

Contents

Acknowledgements

Afos Ltd., Manor Estate, Analby, Hull, Yorks.
Central Electricity Generating Board, South Western Region.
Edward Baker Ltd, Cornard Mills, Sudbury, Suffolk.
Bilal Khan.
Mr. G.L. Powell.
Savack Service Ltd, 145 Sterte Road, Pool, Dorset.
Thomson & Joseph Ltd, Castle House, 21 Davey Place, Norwich, NR2 1PJ.
Wasser-Chemie Technik, Klauschunke, Schloss, Bergheim, D-3593 Edertal 1, West Germany.

Monochrome Illustrations

Full Colour Illustrations

Introduction

The purpose of this book is to serve as a guide to the person who wishes to breed fish as a profitable hobby. It is not intended to be a manual for the prospective fish-farmer, although this subject is briefly covered also.

As with any other worthwhile interest, it is experience which brings success, and whilst this can only be attained the hard way, it is hoped that this book will assist the fish-breeder, and help him to avoid some of the elementary errors.

It is assumed that the reader has a pond of some sort available, either a small ornamental one in his or her garden, or even a larger one, possibly a lake. If not, then instruction is given concerning the making of one.

Perhaps the enthusiast will be content to pursue the hobby in a small way. On the other hand, expansion may follow as he builds on success; another pool, more fish, and his pastime has developed into a full-time occupation. This is how many of today's fish farms have developed.

The amateur who wishes to begin breeding fish may find himself confused regarding which species to rear. The author hopes that in the following chapters he will enable the reader to make a choice. Fish are beautiful creatures, and each breed has its own special attraction. Even the humble common Goldfish, all too often taken for granted as he swims around his small bowl, is a creature of superlative brilliance. Each fish has its own particular characteristics which make it attractive to an enthusiast.

Monetary reward is not the sole factor which persuades a person to take up fish keeping. Yet a hobby which not only pays for itself, but shows a profit at the end of the year, is an added bonus and an incentive to the amateur. Even a supplement to the housekeeping, in the form of fresh fish for the table, is welcome in these days of high food prices and soaring inflation.

1

FISH CULTURE

*Electro-fishing is carried out once a year at spawning time
in order to obtain the eggs for the hatchery*

(Courtesy: Cynrig Salmon Hatchery)

A general view of the hatchery showing the main smolt rearing ponds on the left and fry tanks on the right.

CHAPTER ONE

Fish Culture

Fish culture is the breeding of fish artificially either to produce a food crop, to provide stock for angling or ornamental pools, or to benefit pools and streams by rearing a species which clears harmful vegetation. Many species are complementary to others in a variety of ways. Another aim is to improve a particular breed by introducing fresh stock and thus produce better specimens.

Fish culture was first practised in China many centuries ago. The ancient Chinese placed mats in streams and ponds for the fish to spawn on, and collected the eggs in this way. This, of course, was fish culture at its simplest. The Ancient Romans also bred fish artificially.

But fish culture really got underway in the eighteenth century, and it was introduced into Britain from Norway, beginning with a method of hatching salmon in wooden boxes.

The United States of America were the first to recognise fish culture as a means of increasing a stock of fish for sport. They soon began breeding baitfish (minnows) in large quantities.

But in order to be really profitable this type of fish breeding must be conducted on a very large scale. Trout have been bred artificially since 1850, but only in recent years has the project really proved its worth.

The most important factor in any type of fish culture is that the water supply should be greater than the minimum requirements. A sudden shortage of water and a consequent fall in the level of the pond will have disastrous results.

Direct spring water is often too cold for propagation, and it should be stored in a reservoir while the temperature rises. It should also be aerated to remove any harmful gases. Yet springs as a source of water are a distinct advantage as long as pollution can be prevented; the water will generally be clearer and purer, and during hot weather it will be cool. However, the use of a spring for propagation itself is not advisable as it will be difficult to eliminate undesirable species of fish and other predators.

Fish culture is an important source of food supply for the future which until comparatively recently has been greatly neglected. Trout farming, for instance, is not simply a method of stocking pools so that anglers can fish them. Many farms supply fresh fish direct to restaurants, the trout on your plate having been killed that same day.

Owners of neglected ponds can purchase quantities of a species which will clear undesirable growth and improve the quality of the water. Ornamental pools can be restocked with good specimens thereby eliminating the problem of inter-breeding among the existing fish.

Let us take a look at how fish culture is expanding throughout the world, its importance being recognised as a vital aspect of increasing a dwindling food supply.

There are already plans to instal a massive hatchery on the shores of Lake Champlain, in Vermont, to rear Atlantic salmon; lake – brown – brook – steelhead –and rainbow trout.

Progress is already being made on a Scottish salmonid project on Loch Kanaird, in Wester Ross. The idea is to buy salmon smolts to be reared on a commercial scale in floating pens on the loch. The fish will be marketed fresh on ice without any artificial preparation other than boxing.

There is a project underway to increase trout and carp production in Pakistan. The fisheries are on Tarbela Lake, and the profit is expected to be in excess of £30,000 within a comparatively short time. Other breeds of carp will be reared here in due course. In addition to this scheme there are seven other government-sponsored fish-rearing programmes in force in northern Pakistan.

Taiwan has begun exporting eels to West Germany, and this could lead to regular trade between Taiwan and Europe.

During early 1977 some 1,400 fish ponds were constructed in Laos, and training courses in fish management are now being held. The vast water resources are being utilised in this way, and even by 1974 yearly fish production was in the region of 20,000 tons.

Fish farming research centres have been set up in Bangladesh, incorporating more than 8,000 ponds, and already the production has reached 800,000 tons of fish per annum, with exports earning about £6 million. This government project is likely to receive a US $18 million loan from the Asian Development Bank, and a 40,000 ton increase in fish production is expected by 1984.

The Fishery Agency of the Japanese Ministry of Agriculture and Forestry has set aside 75 billion yen towards fish farming in coastal areas. The existing projects for sea ranching of salmon are to have their hatchery capacity increased from 1.4 billion to 2 billion eggs.

There are plans to begin farming freshwater prawns on the island of Dominica in the Caribbean. The initial farm is to be sited at Azraq, fifty miles east of Amman.

In Sweden, freshwater crayfish are being bred in a disused quarry near Orebro. The fact that they are being reared 130 feet underground means that they are immune to the disease which has killed off the local Swedish species. The crayfish grow to about 4cm in this quarry, and they are then taken to lakes where they grow to 9cm before being marketed. One scheme is to breed faster-growing and larger crayfish.

New Zealand's mussel farms are increasing their production with a 500 ton 1977 harvest. While eel and trout projects have failed, salmon ranching is in the process of being developed. The USSR, however, has a scheme for mussel cultivation in the Barents Sea. This will be in Zelenetskaya Zapadnaya Bay and should yield about 3,000 tons each season. Ten thousand ponds are planned, with about two kilos of mussels in each.

A fish and prawn farm is being planned in Brunei, southeast Asia, and will be the largest in the world, rearing the most prolific of all freshwater prawns, *Macrobrachium rosenbergii*.

Fish production in Hungary is predicted to increase following larger pond yields. Spawning places will be set up to produce fry for specialised fish-farms, and many of the existing farms will have been modernised by 1980.

Czechoslovakia's fish production, mostly carp, yielded a record 12,600 metric tons in 1977.

Of course, we are dealing here with fish culture at national level, far more advanced and on a larger scale than anything which the reader could possibly hope to achieve. **But these facts and figures demonstrate the importance of artificial fish-breeding on the world market.** The ratio of increase can be applied to our own smaller efforts, though. We can expand, build another pond, and breed and sell more fish. The reward will be in the satisfaction of a job well done, theory put into practice, experiments that have succeeded, and, most important of all, an accumulation of experience as one season follows another. Past mistakes will not be repeated, and in time the reader will become an expert in his chosen field.

SMALL SCALE FISH-FARMING AT LOW COST

The beginner may well ask, "But how do I make a start?" Well, everybody has to start with little or no knowledge in most enterprises, and in the initial stages fish breeding will present an immense number of problems, but these can be overcome with perseverance. Experience is the key to suc-

cess in any walk of life, and it is no different in the case of
fish-farming. The reader must learn from his mistakes, and
ensure that he does not make the same mistake twice. Much
trial and error will be involved, and thus it is best to begin in
a small way so that the losses will not be too heavy. The following is a brief summary of much which will be explained
in greater detail in later chapters, a basis on which the amateur can work.

Ponds

Ponds need not be costly and basic materials can provide a
first breeding pool. An available source of water can be utilised profitably. Quite a few private gardens in rural areas
have streams passing either through them or in close proximity. It must be stressed that it is an offence to stem the flow
of any such waterway, but permission can usually be
obtained to divert the course of a brook over a few yards. For
trout breeding running water is vital and this can be
achieved by building your pool so that the stream passes in
and out of it, with grids at the inlet and outlet to prevent
your own fish from disappearing into the brook as well as
stopping predators and waste matter from damaging your
pool and stock.

The rearing of trout is not difficult, and a pool 12 feet
long by 6 feet wide and 2 feet deep should be large enough to
begin with. These measurements, however, should be
regarded as the *minimum* size. The pond can be dug out and
lined with PVC sheeting if the ground itself will not hold
water. The main drawback with artificial pools, of this type,
is that they will be devoid of vegetation, and it is imperative
to establish a certain amount of growth in the water before
introducing fish. Plant life can be transported from natural
ponds, and planted in the soil which covers the polythene;
they will soon grow and spread. It will not be very long
before Whirligig beatles take up residence, an advantage to
any pool. These insects are apparently attracted to stretches

of water during periods of bright moonlight.

An aerator is an item of equipment which the amateur should purchase (unless he is skilled in engineering and electronics when he might be able to make one). This device will maintain the required amount of oxygen in the water at all times. It is useful in both summer and winter. In summer the warm water will contain less oxygen than in cold weather, and during severe spells the aerator helps to prevent the pond from becoming frozen solid.

Trout breeding

Trout begin to breed in December, and at this time of the year the females should be stripped of their eggs at weekly periods, a method which is explained in greater detail later in this book.

It will take approximately 14 months for the eggs to grow into edible fish, and during this time the breeder must look after his charges carefully.

Rather than involve himself in the more complicated procedure of taking eggs from adult females, hatching them into fry, and then rearing them to fully grown trout, the novice would be advised to purchase fingerlings (small fish) from a *reliable* fish-farm. They will cost only a few pence each and it will give him an insight into fish-breeding more simply. A disastrous experience with hatching could cause him to abandon the whole project without really having explored it properly.

The pond should be stocked at the ratio of 1lb of fish to every cubic foot of water. Special foods are available which contain the right proportion of protein, but this may be unprofitable for the breeder who begins in a very small way. A bulk buy, although economical if used on a large scale, would be wasted in the case of the beginner with a hundred or so fingerlings. Furthermore, this food does not keep indefinitely, and will not store satisfactorily until he expands his operations. Chopped lights with a little liver added will suf-

fice, **but the most important factor is not to overfeed. Stale
food will pollute the water and the fish will die**.

There are two main diseases which are fatal to trout:

Pancreatic Necrosis, contracted by young fry.
Furunculosis, which kills fully grown trout and is
brought into the pool by wild fish — another reason for
having an effective grill on both the inlet and outlet.

Carp breeding

The breeding of Carp is steadily becoming more profitable in England as the species is now accepted on hotel and
restaurant menus. Previously its popularity had been confined to the continent, particularly Germany.

Carp require a water temperature of around 20°C. in
spring if they are to breed successfully. They also like stagnant water, which overcomes a lot of problems for the amateur.

They are easily reared in a garden pool, but will be more
productive if that pool is in an outbuilding which will maintain a warmer water temperature. If the reader has a large
greenhouse on his premises, with some surplus space in it, a
small pool could be constructed on the lines already
described, using PVC to line it.

Carp are much cheaper to feed than trout, and will devour
boiled potatoes, potato peelings and waste bread, although
if bred on a larger scale it will be necessary to buy commercial food.

Possibly one of the reasons why Carp have taken so long
to establish themselves amongst the edible fish in this country is because of a 'muddy' flavour which is sometimes
noticeable after they have been cooked. It is best if they are
put into clean water for two or three days before being
killed. This will remove all remnants of the flavour of their
former habitat.

All waste should be eliminated, wherever possible, if fish-breeding is to be worthwhile and profitable. Even the remains of fish after filleting can be utilised by grinding it up to feed many species. The surplus can be stored in a deep-freeze until it is required.

MARKETING AND EATING YOUR FISH

The end product will determine whether or not fish-rearing is profitable. There is generally a steady market for the ornamental species but the edible varieties need to be offered for sale in a form which will command the best price. Likewise, if you are merely rearing for your own table then you require a product which is more than just edible. It needs to be palatable to such an extent that you will feel that all your efforts over the previous months have been justifiably rewarded.

SMOKING

Again, this is dealt with in detail later, but the d-i-y enthusiast might well decide that he can make a fish-smoker for himself.

Basically, a smoker saves waste. A surplus of fish can be stored for later eating or for sale, and a freshly caught fish can be put on the table in a most appetising way.

There are two methods of smoking:

Hot smoking, which both smokes and *cooks*, and is really designed for smaller quantities of fish.

Cold smoking, a method of preserving a bulk of fish for storage.

The container in which the fish is to be smoked needs to be fireproof. The casing of an old cooker or refrigerator will suffice with a little modification.

Hot Smoking

The floor should be covered with wood dust, above which should be a raised sheet of metal, an inch or so above the dust, to prevent the direct heat from scorching the fish

10

which can be placed upon a grid on top of the metal sheet. Shallow pans (tin lids are ideal) are necessary for the methylated spirit or solid fuel tablets. Wood dust is obtainable from firms who supply commercial smokers. Three tablespoonfuls are advised for a light smoking, six for the fish which are required for storage.

Cold Smoking

Whereas for hot smoking the cooker needs to be partitioned off so that the fish becomes cooked as well, with cold smoking the temperature must not exceed 90°F. This can be achieved by removing the sectional plate and fixing the grid(s) further up the container. However, if the temperature is too low the food will not be preserved. An average of 85°F should be ideal.

Cold smoking does not preserve foods entirely. In order to achieve the correct degree of preservation the fish should be soaked in brine at the rate of one hour per pound of fish. (*See* Figure 1 and Chapter 3, pp 34-38.)

Fish-breeding plays a large part in self-sufficiency and even if the object of the breeder is not entirely a monetary reward then he must appreciate the saving concerned in relation to buying fish for the table from fishmongers and supermarkets. Records should be kept of expenditure and income (monies received from sales, or fish provided for the household). These figures will show how worthwhile the project is, and in addition to this the beginner has embarked upon an absorbing hobby.

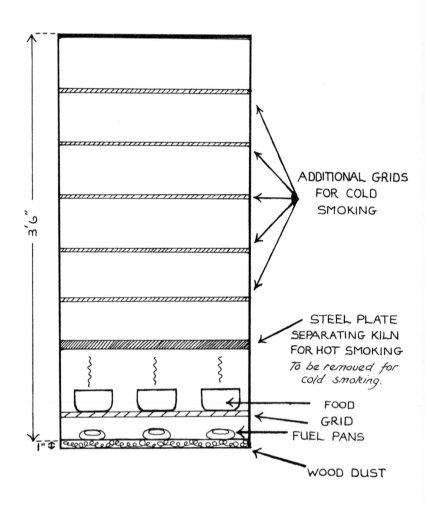

ADDITIONAL GRIDS
FOR COLD
SMOKING

STEEL PLATE
SEPARATING KILN
FOR HOT SMOKING
*To be removed for
cold smoking.*

FOOD
GRID
FUEL PANS

WOOD DUST

3'6"

1"

*Figure 1 'Hot' and 'Cold' smoking kiln made from an old
cooker or fridge.*

12

2
POND CONSTRUCTION

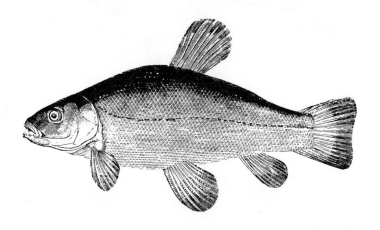

Tench (Tinca vulgaris).

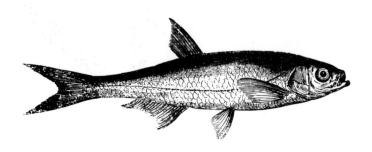

Bleak.

CHAPTER TWO

Pond Construction

The most important factor in any form of fish culture is, of course, water. Without water it would be impossible to keep or breed fish. Even so, some thought must be given to the pond or larger pool for your proposed venture. It is not sufficient merely to make use of some existing expanse of water and hope that it will suffice. Such failure to pay attention to detail could prove very costly.

The following are species which live and breed best in a certain type of water:

Still Water Carp (all species), Golden Orf'e, Goldfish, Perch, Pikeperch, Char, Brook Char, Pike, Gudgeon, Tench, Golden Rudd, Cisco, Eel, Stickleback.
Running Water Trout (all species), Grayling, Bleak.
Freshwater (running)/saltwater Salmon.

It is no good, for instance, hoping that trout will survive in a pool without running water. If you do not have a suitable tract of water on your land, then you must endeavour to create one. Some of the best pools in this country have been artifically constructed, and the author has made several for his own use. Before we look at the more expensive types of pools which can be purchased, let us first consider making one.

LARGE POOL
(Approximately 40m x 12m, suitable for fish that are

accustomed to living in still water).

A pool of this nature is better situated on high ground where there is less danger of storms washing silt and debris into it. Any excessive flow of water in and out of the pool will remove natural food and lower the temperature which should be between 60-80°F.

Having chosen your site, dig a couple of holes, say about a yard square and a foot deep. The purpose of this is to ascertain whether or not the ground will hold water without any artificial lining. Usually this only happens on low, boggy ground, but it is well worth a try. Wait until there has been a period of rain, and then inspect these holes. If they are full of water do not immediately presume that your problem is solved. Sometimes it takes several days for water to drain away, even in porous soil.

If, after a week of comparatively dry weather, your holes are still holding water it may be safe to assume that your pond will do likewise, but it is wiser to bide your time and check the levels daily. A very slow seepage could result in the amateur fish-breeder having a whole batch of fish stranded on dry land!

In all likelihood your pool will not hold water, so a lining will be necessary, but first we must concentrate on digging out the structure of the pool. For this it will be imperative to hire a bulldozer (or mechanical digger). At the time of writing the author has just made such a pool and the cost of bulldozing was £5 per hour, plus £20 for the transportation of the machine on a low-loader from a town six miles away. It took eight hours to complete the excavations at a total cost of £60, which is quite reasonable by today's prices.

Mark out the site, but do not simply leave your bulldozer man to do the job on his own. Very few of them have dug a pool, and they are apt to think that any large hole will suffice. *Use a spirit-level* to ensure that the bottom is even, otherwise problems could arise, and a large area might be wasted because the water will run down to one end.

16

Figure 2 The author's pool shortly after completion, before water was fed into it.

Pay attention to the banks. The excavated soil needs to be distributed as evenly as possible and the banks must be secure enough to hold the weight of several thousand gallons of water.

The author's pool was constructed on a steep gradient, and the first task was to bulldoze a level shelf on the hillside. This was accomplished quite easily, but the largest bank had to be on the lower side to withstand torrential rain gushing downhill. An avalanche would have ruined the whole project.

Make as neat a job as possible, and try to construct the pool as symmetrically as you can for it will make the job of lining it so much easier.

Having excavated the pool to your satisfaction it is advisable to fence it against stock, for any animal wallowing in the water will undoubtedly puncture your PVC lining. On the area in question the author saved money by making a hawthorn hedge serve as a fence on one side, and had to protect only the three remaining sides. Make the fence sound by using the best materials. Tannalised stakes are best as they last for about 25 years, and pig-netting is more durable than sheep netting, and is equally as effective with minimal difference in price.

The pool is dug and fenced. The next job is to line it. A silage sheet can be purchased from almost any agricultural supplier and the standard size of 40m x 12.8m is ideal for this pool. The sheet is supplied in a roll, but it is folded several times to facilitate transportation, so the reader will be well advised to unroll it *in a smooth field on a windless day*, and then re-roll it so that it can be unfolded easily across the full length of the pool.

Check the surface of your pool, and rake off any sharp stones which might puncture the PVC. There will be an immense weight pressing down on it once it fills with water. As an added precaution it is a good idea to lay empty polythene fertilizer bags (which most farmers will be only too

Plate 2   Rainbow Trout   *(From painting by Jim Dunford.)*

Figure 3 The author's pool after the first thunderstorm.

pleased to get rid of) in the bottom, and then roll the silage sheet on to them. The bags can be split and opened out if you do not have enough to cover the surface unopened. This is an additional precaution against the PVC being punctured from beneath, and it could even save you a leak by plugging a hole.

Do not walk about on the PVC once you begin unrolling it. Unroll about a yard on to the polythene bags, and then begin fetching soil from the banks in a wheelbarrow. It will be necessary to use much of the excavated earth to spread a layer on the PVC, but take it evenly from the banks so that they are not demolished in any one area. Again, this soil must be checked as you fill the barrow, removing any large stones. Spread it gently. A thin covering is sufficient; just enough so that some growth may be started in the pool. Without the soil distributed thus you will have a 'lifeless' pool, devoid of vegetation except on the banks.

The silage sheet will reach about two thirds of the way up the banks. Once the laying has been finished one can walk along the banks and gently rake soil downwards so that the exposed ends of PVC are buried.

There are still a few things that can be done to improve your pool. Vegetation should be planted around the edges; a few clumps of reeds taken from an existing pool, and perhaps some grass seed sown on the bare banks.

All that we are short of now is the water. In the author's case he has to rely on rainwater, although it would be possible to use the overflow from the small private reservoir which serves his house. If there is no hurry to fill the pool then the heavens will oblige in due course.

The question of depth of water is a very important one. It should be deep enough to prevent the fish from freezing in winter. The author's pool has a depth of 4-5 feet at one end, and 18 inches at the other. This should be ample.

Every pond needs draining and cleaning out periodically, and therefore it is best if the breeder has more than one. Eco-

Pl. 4. 3. Male Salmon (*Teme gairistics 1. For D. after)*

nomically, though, this is not always possible.

It may be of interest to the reader to note the cost of making this pool:

	£ p
Bulldozer	60.00
24 tannalised stakes	14.16
Silage sheet 40m x 12.8m	41.43
2 rolls of pig-netting	30.58
Staples for fencing	1.50
Labour employed	29.00
Total	176.67

MAKING A SMALL FISH POND

Let us, in contrast, consider the making of a small ornamental fish-pond, the kind which is to be found in many gardens, usually containing goldfish.

They are easy to make and very inexpensive. As with the larger pool, first it has to be dug out. The size will be determined by the number of fish which you intend to keep in it. 6 feet long by 4 feet wide and 18 inches deep should comfortably house a dozen goldfish. One interesting point to note is that goldfish grow according to the size of the pond or tank in which they are kept. Thus one housed permanently in a small bowl indoors will rarely grow to more than 2½ inches, whilst one in a pond, the size of which we are contemplating, will probably attain 4 inches, perhaps more.

This pond, of course, has to be dug out by hand, and care must be taken to see that the sides are straight and the bottom level. Allow a few inches in excess of your pond measurements because you will be concreting it to a thickness of about 3 inches.

It would be perfectly possible to use PVC sheeting to make your pond, but the effect would be spoiled. Anyway, the small area involved would hardly be worth this labour- and time-saving method.

Once the cement has set, it can be effectively sealed with 'Aquaseal', a varnish-like substance obtainable from most ironmongers. Remember, though, that to introduce fish straightaway into the pond is a sure way of killing them. Concrete is poisonous to fish during the first few months, and to be absolutely safe it is advisable to wait twelve months.

The author once made such a pond in his garden set against the unsightly mound of an underground air-raid shelter. The latter he planted with 'ground cover' (aubretia, etc.), but from the summit, going right down to the pond, he built a series of steps in the manner of a miniature waterfall. In this way the rain water cascaded down into the pool below.

After twenty years this pond is still holding water without any renovation whatsoever having been carried out.

Butyl pond liners

Butyl is possibly the best material with which to line a small pond although it is much more expensive than PVC sheeting. Butyl is tough, has an extensive life, and in addition one is able to seal a join by means of welding. Very pliable, it will form more easily into the shape of the pond, and is less likely to tear with normal use than polythene or PVC.

However, the cost of butyl is prohibitive for use in other than small ponds, and the reader contemplating expansion will probably wish to begin with PVC as this will be the material which he will use most widely. In most cases cement will be adequate to construct a small ornamental pond of a permanent nature.

COMMERCIAL POOLS AND PONDS

Nowadays, pools and ponds of almost any size can be purchased and installed. The following are but a few of the varieties on the market, and the prospective fish-breeder with

22

Figure 4 H-T-T suspended cloth pools.

some capital to spare can be sure of finding the pool to suit his requirements.

The following information on suspended cloth ponds has been kindly supplied by Messrs. Wasser-Chemie Technik, Klauschunke, Schloss, Hergheim, D-3593 Edertal 1, West Germany:

H-T-T suspended cloth ponds: the new system which reduces costs and labour while raising productivity

Design

The suspended cloth ponds consist of a framework of hot-galvanized pipe on which a special cloth is freely suspended. This material is both pliable and of high tenacity, so that the fishes will not be injured. When filled with water it hangs in an inverted arch from the framework. It is closed at the top with a net cover. The mesh size of the net is fine enough to provide extensive shade, prevent penetration by dirt and animal pests and keep the fishes from leaping over the side. The net cover is stretched over the pond and hangs $2/3$ rds the way down the sides. A strong rubber band around the edge of the net keeps it taut. The outlet of the H-T-T is a screened overflow pipe. The pipe has a diameter of 250mm and a height of 750mm; the strainer closure may have varying hole sizes. The drain pot of glass-fibre-reinforced plastic is installed at the lowest point and has a 150mm diameter pipe connection. It may be connected with a PVC spiral hosepipe 160mm in diameter to remove the fish without injuring them.

Suitable locations

The H-T-T system can be set up anywhere where water is available. It is especially suitable for areas in which aquatic animals could not normally be kept, such as near unused mountain streams and at the seashore.

The proximity of power stations is also advantageous,

Figure 5 H-T-T suspended cloth pools.

because it is easy to make profitable use of their cooling
water. In addition to these fish culture applications the
H-T-T is also excellent for temporarily keeping live fish of
every kind.

The cloth material

This material is an essential feature of the H-T-T system.
It is made of Trevira high tenacity fabric coated on both
sides with PVC. Trevira high tenacity is the name of the
polyester filament which was especially developed by
Hoechst for technical applications and has proven its worth
in many years of service and in over 400 different products.

The PVC-coated Trevira high tenacity fabric is waterproof, resistant to weathering, rotproof and also resistant to
corrosion and ageing, so that it has a long service life. The
material requires no maintenance and its flexibility prevents clogging.

25

Sizes

The system is built in 5 different lengths — from 3 to 10m. All sizes are 1.5m wide, hold water at a depth of 0.75m and are 0.96m high overall.

Space requirements

In the open: because of its low space requirements the H-T-T system with 150-200 units occupies only 1 hectare of open land.

Indoors: the H-T-T is designed in such a way that it can be installed in 3 or more tiers without difficulty. This leads to a great reduction in the floor space required.

Functional design

The net cover provides adequate shade and keeps the fishes quiet and more willing to consume nourishment. At the same time it protects them from predators. Since the H-T-T ponds are suspended above the ground the fishes cannot be disturbed by earth-borne sound waves.

In contrast to conventional pond systems, no losses are caused by flushing and washing operations and the ponds do not become clogged with plant growth or filamentous algae that could interfere with the removal of the fishes.

Work operations

Since the H-T-T is narrow and readily accessible, checks on the behaviour and health of the animals can be carried out easily and regularly. There are no problems encountered in draining the ponds, removing the fish or rinsing out excrement and remnants of feed, since a high flow rate is attained in the drain pot. The H-T-Ts are self-cleaning. It is also easy to install automatic feeders.

Maintenance

Two special design features facilitate maintenance operations: first the ponds are accessible from every side, and secondly, the table-top height makes it possible to work without bending. The rounded-trough shape of the suspended fabric means that the H-T-T has a low point running its entire length, in which excrement and feed residues

26

collect. From there they are continuously rinsed out by the inflowing water.

Changing location

All the various programmes of the H-T-T system require only two different pipe lengths for the framework. The lengths of 90 and 150cm were chosen to give a handy size to work with and to avoid confusion during assembly and disassembly. The design of the drain is the same for every pond type, which is a further simplification. Disassembled and packed for transport, the cloth pond makes a small package that requires little space and can easily be stowed in a normal car. That means incomparable mobility is achieved without great cost.

Assembly and disassembly

The uncomplicated design, employing only a few simple parts, affords rapid assembly and disassembly and eliminates the need for a building permit. Even when larger H-T-T units are set up, only a few days of assembly are required before fish breeding can begin. Where the ground is extremely wet and soft it can be covered with perforated metal plates before the ponds are erected.

Stability and strength

All leg pipes are provided with adjustable jackscrews and ground plates. It is thus possible to adjust the H-T-T to the correct height on uneven ground. On some types of ground it may be necessary to place an additional plate under the framework feet to prevent the feet from sinking in. When the system is correctly assembled it is so solid and stable that it cannot be upset even by several persons.

Shelter structures

Suspended cloth ponds require no shelter, but to make work easier and when the ponds are arranged in several tiers, it is advisable to provide a protective shed. Aluminium tent sheds are available for this purpose: lightweight shed structures with a span of 8 to 28m. A maintenance-free anodized aluminium framework is covered with PVC-coated

Trevira high tenacity fabric, which is also resistant to weathering and ageing as well as being rotproof. These sheds are designed in accordance with the module construction system which allows them to be expanded or reduced in size by any amount at any time. A foundation is not needed nor is a building permit required.

Productivity

When erected on only one level, 150 to 200 H-T-T basins require only 1 hectare of open ground. With the fish/water ratio at 1:30 an annual capacity of 50 tonnes of fish protein per hectare can be attained, and where there is ample good fish water that figure can be raised to 100 t/ha. Correspondingly higher production is attained when a 3-tier arrangement is used. In comparison the conventional system requires long construction times before production can begin and an area of 50 ha is required to produce the same number of fishes. The productivity of the H-T-T system can be further increased by automatic control of the lighting to vary the intensity, the cycles of light and dark, the duration of darkness, dawn and dusk and duration of the period of greatest brightness.

Worldwide patent protection has been applied for.

Water treatment container: Schunke circulating system

The water treatment container continuously produces fish water of the highest biological quality. It enables the hatching of the fish spawn and the safe rearing of the delicate fry. The water treatment container is fitted with time-tested machinery, equipment and materials of noted German industrial companies.

Programme includes the planning and delivery of fish farms in accordance with international standards for every quantity and type of fish production, for fresh and salt water fishes, and cold and warm water animals. From spawn through fingerlings up to the market stage advice is given on selling and marketing, business analyses are prepared, profitability calculations and feeding plans, and advisory services are provided throughout the course of production.

Summary

The H-T-T system was developed for use by nuclear power stations, factories utilizing fish products, pond-fish cultivators, sideline operations, forestry business, mine operators, fishing clubs and for the trade to keep live fishes temporarily. This system reduces the amount of labour required and the operating costs for keeping fish.

The H-T-T system is cost-saving in comparison with rigid breeding basins and the conventional pond system.

The comparatively low space requirements considerably raise the production rate per unit of area. Productivity can be further increased by automatic lighting control.

The simple design employing only a few parts makes for quick and easy assembly and disassembly and problem-free transport requiring minimal space.

Controls, work operations and maintenance are greatly facilitated by well-thought-out, practical design characteristics and auxiliary equipment.

Materials have been used which have proven their worth in other applications and products under rugged conditions and so guarantee a long service life.

With the H-T-T system the promising future of pond-fish culture has already begun.

A single incubator showing the eggs and filtration pipe.

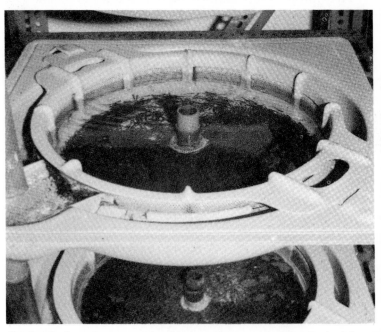

A single incubator with alevins, the newly-hatched fish.

(Courtesy: Cynrig Salmon Hatchery)

3

GENERAL FISH
MANAGEMENT

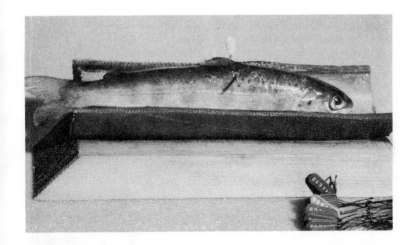

STAGES IN TAGGING (see page 87)
1. The smolt is anaesthetised.

2. *Then the tag is attached by nylon threads.*

3. *The tagged smolt just before regaining consciousness and being returned to the tank.*

CHAPTER THREE

General Fish Management

One of the objects of fish management is to improve the breed, and often artificially reared fish are superior to those bred in the wild. For instance, trout will grow more rapidly in a pond (provided there is water running in and out of it) than in a stream.

DANGER FROM PREDATORS

Possibly the most important factor in any breeding pond is to see that it has **cover**. There must always be ample vegetation, both for food and for protection from predators. A heron which finds a pool with little or no cover will clear it of every fish within a matter of a few days. It is capable of eating around thirty fish per day. Last century, when pole-traps were still legal, water-bailiffs often set them in the shallows to catch herons. Cruel as this may be, it is interesting to note that a heron caught by the leg will almost invariably vomit its catch. Likewise, a kingfisher will constantly raid pools with an abundance of fish in them. These spectacular birds are comparatively tame, and the author knows of one case where a kingfisher fished unconcernedly only yards from where an angler sat on a river bank.

POACHING

Poaching, however, is something much more serious, and large trout or salmon hatcheries are forced to maintain nocturnal vigilance. The rearer on a small scale is less likely to be troubled by the larger gangs, but there is always the possibility of a local poacher visiting the pool after dark to obtain a fish for his supper. Over a period of time this can be quite costly, and one or two alarm-guns of the kind used by gamekeepers in their pheasant preserves are a good investment.

EQUIPMENT

First let us look at various items of equipment. The reader must be fully organised before making a start. It is useless to go out and purchase a quantity of fry, deposit them in some area of water, and hope that they will live and breed in it. In all probability they will be dead within a matter of hours, and in addition to time wasted, the experiment will have proved costly. **Good equipment is an investment.**

FISH SMOKING

Where it is the reader's aim to breed fish for food, then it is important that some thought is given to preparation for the table. A badly cooked fish will deter him from trying again, in many cases, and he may even abandon fish culture altogether. Where trout and salmon are concerned it will be necessary to have some idea of fish smoking and the following information has been kindly supplied by Afos Ltd, Manor Estate, Analby, Hull, from whom further information and these kilns for smoking small quantities of fish can be obtained.

The Torry Mini-Kiln

The kiln is supplied as a complete unit and is pre-wired ready for connection to the mains supply.

The most convenient method is to stand the kiln on a bench approximately 30 inches high with a hinged extension for accommodating the trolley. The table should be capable of carrying the loaded weight of the kiln (approximately 4cwt) and the hinged extension (weight of a maximum loaded trolley, 80lb.

The 5 inch chimney should be extended to a suitable point outside the building and a 13amp electric supply connected to the terminals provided.

Ancilliary Equipment

A small trolley is supplied which has runners for seven trays for the smoking of products such as golden cutlets, kipper fillets, salmon and cod roes; a set of twelve stainless steel banjoes for hanging white fish fillets; a set of stainless steel speats for hanging finnan haddocks, buckling, trout or bloaters; a set of twelve wooden tenters for kippers; a plastic brine tube with a capacity of five gallons and two packets of colouring, one for white fish and one for kippers.

The fish have to be prepared for smoking in the normal manner by washing, cutting, brining and hanging.

Controls

The controls of the kiln are very simple to operate. One sliding damper in the chimney controls the fresh air inlet and the amount of wet smoke exhausted up the chimney. The electricity supply required is one 13 amp socket, 230-240 volts A.C.

A small fan draws the smoke from a three-tiered smoke box over the product and a chimney on the pressure side of the fan vents the wet smoke to the atmosphere.

The temperature of the kiln is controlled by a thermostat operating a bank of electric heaters. The heaters are operated through a rotary switch giving a selection of one, two or three kilowatts, as required.

Smoke Producers

The smoke is produced from burning wood shavings and sawdust in a three tiered smoke producer, which is an integral part of the kiln. This smoke producer is arranged in the form of three pull-out drawers; this facilitates the laying of the fires and the emptying of the ash. Each drawer has a set

35

of hit-and-miss holes which are used to control the draught on the fires and hence the quantity of smoke produced.

In most cases the fish are brined in an 80% strength brine. This brine is made up in the plastic tub by adding 8lb of vacuum dried salt to 3 gallons (30lb) of water. When the salt has dissolved this quantity of brine is sufficient for the brining of four stones (56lb) of fish in two batches of two stones (28lb). If more fish are to be brined, a little salt should be added to make up to the strength. If colouring is required for white fish fillets or cutlets, 1 cupful of the following should be added to every 3 gallon batch of brine. Dissolve 8 ounces of the lemon dye in 1 gallon of hot water, add when cool and 1 cupful to the 3 gallons of brine. In each case stir the brine with the added colouring thoroughly before immersing the fish. The solution of dye will keep indefinitely but the brine should be made up daily.

For the preparation of the fish and brining times, *see Torry Kiln Operator's Handbook* (see acknowledgements for address).

Hanging

After brining the fish are hung to drip before smoking. For white fish products the longer the dripping time, the better the gloss that will be formed. During warm weather it is better to store the trolley of fish in a chill room for dripping. Never leave brined fish in contact with each other, or they will stick together when parted.

Smoking

For most cures in this kiln only one fire is required. Two fires can be laid for smoking salmon and lit one at a time. The hot smoked products such as trout, buckling, and eels will require three fires. The fires are laid as follows:

1 Remove the drawers from the kiln.
2 Place a strip of paper or wood wool along the front of the drawers covering the hit-and-miss holes.
3 Cover the bottom of the drawer with a layer of wood

Plate 5.   Crucian Carp. (From a painting by Miss Dewhurst.)

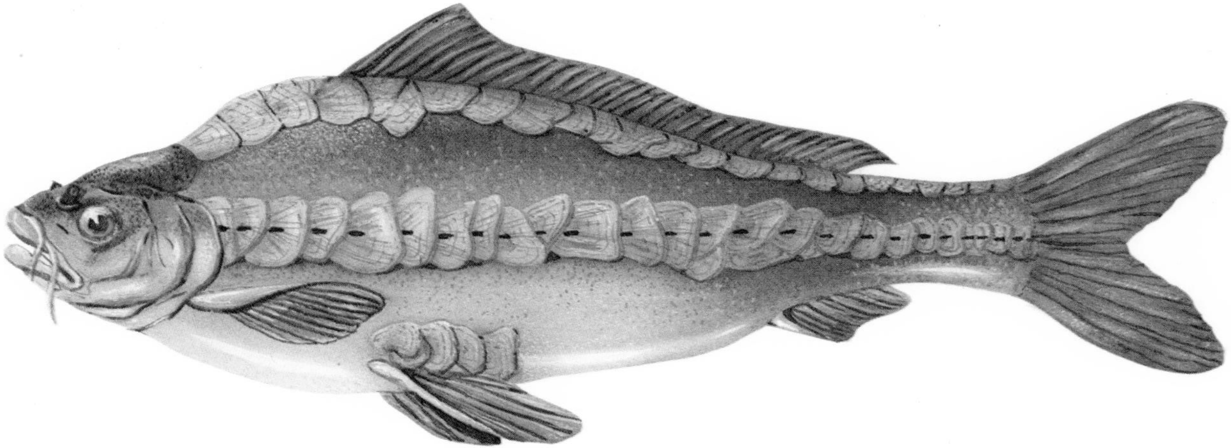

Plate 6 Mirror Carp *(From painting by Jim Dunford.)*

chips or wood shavings to a depth of 2 inches.

4 Cover the wood chips with sawdust (not too dry) to a depth of 2-3 inches, leaving the front inch of wood or chips free of sawdust.

5 Replace the drawers in the kiln and the fires are now ready to light.

OPERATION OF THE KILN — COLD SMOKING

1 Set the thermostat temperature to 80°F. This is the temperature required for the smoking of kippers, kipper fillets, all white fish products and salmon.

2 Switch on the circulating fan.

3 Pull out slide in chimney to full extent.

4 Light one fire.

5 Close the hit-and-miss holes in the front of the drawer.

6 Push in the slide in the chimney until smoke escapes through the front of the drawers, and then slowly open the slide until the smoke just disappears. The air inlet damper will now be about a quarter open.

7 Switch on all heaters until operating temperature is reached and then reduce to 1 kw.

These settings will cure the following:

3½ stones (49 lb) of kipper fillets on trays.
4 stones (56 lb) of finnan haddock on speats.
4 stones (56 lb) of kippers on tenter sticks.
3½ stones (49 lb) of haddock or whiting cutlets on trays.
3 stones (42 lb) of cod or haddock fillets on banjoes.
20 sides of salmon grilse on trays.

The times of curing these products are as suggested in the Torry Kiln Operator's Handbook, and the trolley of fish has to be turned round at the half time cure.

OPERATIONS OF THE KILN — HOT SMOKING

The two main products for hot smoking are trout and herring for buckling. The kiln will hold 5 stones (70 lb) of these fish on speats. The fish are prepared as in the Torry Kiln Operator's Handbook. The two additional sets of rails will have to be fitted to the trolley for the trout, as the speats have to be placed running from back to front of the kiln. The trout are speated through the bone in the tail end and hang with either the backs or bellies to the air stream. The fish are placed in the kiln wet from the brine and the smoking carried out as follows:

1 Lay the fires and proceed as for cold smoking, leaving all heaters switched on.
2 After the temperature and the one fire has settled down, light a second fire, when the temperature will probably rise to about 90°F.
3 After smoking at 90°F for one hour, raise the thermostat setting to 120°F and light the third fire. Close down exhaust damper until the air inlet is in the closed position.
4 After a further one hour at 120°F raise the thermostat setting to 170°F and at the end of a further hour the fish should have sufficient colour and be cooked.

MAINTENANCE

It is recommended that weekly cleaning is carried out if the kiln is in daily use.

1 Isolate the electricity supply at mains.
2 Remove all smoke producer drawers, air inlet stabiliser and front access panel.
3 Remove inlet diffuser wall. This is retained by a single locking screw at the top and is located into a channel at the base of the kiln.
4 Clean all internal surfaces, removing tar deposits, firstly with a scraper, then scrub clean using a mild soda solution. Pay particular attention to the diffuser

wall, fan impellor and smoke deflector section. This is located inside the kiln behind the diffuser wall position, on top of the smoke producer drawers.

5 Reassemble all sections, ensuring diffuser wall is located correctly.

6 Check that the fresh air stabiliser is freely moving and, if necessary, add a drop of oil on each bearing. Occasionally oil exhaust damper slide and door hinges. The motor bearings should be lubricated twice yearly with Shell Voluta 27 or similar grade of oil.

MOVING OR TRANSPORTING FISH

Anaesthetics and Tranquilizers

One problem which has possibly not occurred to the reader so far is that of moving fish from one pond to another. For instance, the breeder lucky enough to own two ponds will need to transfer his fish to one whilst cleaning out the other. In small pools a net may be used to catch them up, but this method would not be practical in a large one. The fish must be transferred quickly and with a minimum amount of handling. An anaesthetic which has no adverse effect is the answer, and the author is grateful to Messrs. Thomson & Joseph Ltd, Castle House, 21 Davey Place, Norwich, for allowing him to include MS-222 Sandoz in this book.

During his search for a reliable synthetic substitute for cocaine, Maurice Sandoz synthesized meta-aminobenzoic acid ethylester. This substance was classified as a local anaesthetic and found some use in human medicine. However its special characteristics as an anaesthetic and tranquilizer for cold-blooded organisms was soon recognized and, recently, more extensive work in this field has led to renewed interest in this substance, MS-222 Sandoz.

The value of an anaesthetic to temporarily immobilize fish, frogs, and other cold-blooded animals during various procedures — transportation, hatching, weighing, tagging, measuring, research, photography — has long been recognized. A substance suitable for such academic or commercial procedures must be easy to handle, prompt and intense in its action, rapidly reversible in effect and harmless to both the organisms being treated and the men handling it. MS-222 Sandoz satisfies all these requirements. Many fish hatcheries, marine laboratories, universities, governmental agencies, pet industries and fish transporters have begun to use MS-222 Sandoz routinely as the anaesthetic and tranquilizer of choice. The use of MS-222 Sandoz to combat the unicellular parasites of fish has been recognized recently and thus its range of use is extended considerably.

Chemistry

MS-222 Sandoz is the methanesulphonate of meta-aminobenzoic acid ethylester, or, simply ethyl m-animobenzoate. It is thus an isomer of benzocaine having the formula $C_9H_{11}O_2N + CH_3SO_3H$ and the following structure:

$$\text{[benzene ring]}-NH_2 + CH_3SO_3H$$
$$COOC_2H_5$$

MS-222 Sandoz is a fine white crystalline powder. Its molecular weight is 261.3. Soluble to 11%, it forms clear, colourless acid solutions in water. It melts at 145°-150°C. MS-222 Sandoz leaves only minimum traces of ash and is free from chlorides, sulphates, alkaloids and heavy metals. It loses less than 0.5% of its weight upon heating to 103°C.

Nomenclature

MS-222 Sandoz has been variously reported in the literature as MS-222, TS-222 Sandoz, TS-222, Tricaine-Sandoz, Tricaine Methanesulphonate, Metacaine and Metacaine Methanesulphonate.

Methods of application and advantages

MS-222 Sandoz may be applied in a bath, i.e. immersion

of the fish or small animals into a solution of MS-222 Sandoz. It may be sprayed on the gills of large fish, e.g. sharks or rays, by means of a water pistol, bulb syringe, hand pump, etc. It can be given to larger animals by injection.

Since MS-222 Sandoz is very soluble (1:9) in water it dissolves with equal readiness in sea-water, spring water or ordinary tap water. It can be used in a variety of concentrations from 1:1,000 up to 1:30,000 or more — but is most effective in 1:2,000-1:3,000 solutions. Depending upon the size of fish and the concentration the effect is manifest within 15 seconds. Even 400 lb sharks are anaesthetized within one minute with a 1:1,000 sea-water solution.

MS-222 Sandoz has no effect on ciliary action but its effect on muscular activity is rapid. MS-222 Sandoz has no effect on the motility or fertilizing power of frog spermatazoa.

The recovery time from MS-222 Sandoz anaesthesia is usually brief and complete. Prolonged exposure to MS-222 Sandoz in weak concentrations is not harmful, so that it is of much value in transporting live fish.

Ball and Cowen, in an article in *Nature* entitled "Urethane as a Carcinogen and as an Anaesthetic for Fishes", reviewed the literature in which urethane was implicated as a carcinogen in various species of animals. They pointed out that the use of urethane as a fish anaesthetic should be discontinued. They wrote, "As a substitute, we recommend tricaine methane sulphonate (MS-222 Sandoz), in the light of the fact that no deleterious effects, as with urethane, have been reported following its use so far." They further reviewed the uses and concentrations employed up to now such as, a 1:500 solution for eels (*Anguilla anguilla*), a solution for goldfish, brown trout, *Mollienesia latippina* 1:2,000 and axolotls, and a 1:3,500 solution for *Fundulus heteroclitus*.

Trout toxicity studies

Young trout of 6.5 to 9 cm length (the intensity of the effect is inversely proportional to the size of the fish) were

TABLE I. FROG TOXICITY STUDIES

Substance	Lethal concentration for 50% of the animals (LC 50)
MS-222 Sandoz	1:160 (6.2% solution)
Chlorobutanol	1:550 (1.8% solution)
Pentobarbital sodium	1:285 (3.5% solution)

TABLE II. TROUT TOXICITY STUDIES

	MS-222 Sandoz	Chlorobutanol
Lethal concentration for 50% of fish (LC 50)	1:12,200 (0.082%)	1:3,800 (0.265%)
Maximum concentration tolerated (LC 1)	1:15,900 (0.063%)	1:5,700 (0.175%)
Effective concentration, i.e. producing anaesthesia within 3-4 minutes in 99% of fish (EC 99)	1:25,000 (0.040%)	1:7,600 (0.132%)
Therapeutic index LC 1/EC 99	1.57	1.33

immersed for 15 minutes in solutions of various concentrations of the drug tested and then transferred to fresh tap water.

Thus it is seen that MS-222 Sandoz has a better therapeutic index than chlorobutanol.

Published uses of MS-222 Sandoz

Many publications have already appeared concerning the uses of MS-222 Sandoz. The earlier workers used it mostly as an anaesthetic tool. However it is interesting to see the purposes and concentrations used as well as the organisms employed.

Witschi used MS-222 Sandoz for grafting experiments in tadpoles of *Rana temporaria* and pointed out that his results were better than with 0.03% chlorobutanol solution because much fewer animals were lost. He did not state the concentration used.

In investigating lens regeneration of the larvae of *Triton taeniatus*, Sato used concentrations of 1:3,000. The larvae were completely anaesthetized by immersion, put in Ringer's solution and then operated upon.

Rotmann used MS-222 Sandoz to photograph and make sketches of *Triton taeniatus* and *T. cristatus*. He also used concentrations of 1:3,000. The fish could be held free of movement for up to one hour. Rotmann pointed out that MS-222 Sandoz was free from side and after effects and that the anaesthesia could be repeated as often as desired.

Glücksohn used MS-222 Sandoz during two spawning seasons of *Triton taeniatus* and *Triton cristatus*. Using concentrations of 1:3,000 he anaesthetized the fish daily for periods of 15 minutes. There were only minimal changes in development. In general the anaesthetized fish were somewhat smaller than control fish living under the same conditions. However, the proportions were completely normal. Glücksohn also took advantage of the anaesthesia to make photographs and sketches.

In studying the development and regeneration of the colour pattern of tropical fish, Goodrich and Nichols kept records of the growth and melanophore formation of the anal fin of *Brachydanio rerio* by employing a micro-projection apparatus on fish anaesthetized at various intervals with MS-222 Sandoz.

In his paper, "The Development of a Finyl Plastic Subcutaneous Tag for Trout", Butler reported that MS-222 Sandoz was used very effectively during the tagging operation. A concentration of 500 mg per American gallon (approximately 1:7,500) at 50°F (10°C) prepares fish for the operation within 30 seconds.

As regards pet industries MS-222 Sandoz is applied in several ways to pet or ornamental fish. Although it is useful for immobilizing specimens for examination and for treatment of fungus infections and other localized diseases, its most general use in the field lies in transportation. The technique employed with baitfish also applies to ornamental varieties, making it possible to ship greater numbers of fish in a single container; in many cases by parcel post. Tranquilization by MS-222 Sandoz may also be employed with excellent results in the transportation of pugnacious species such as male Siamese Fighting Fish (Bettas) or the Pirhanas, as Gossington has reported. This technique permits the transportation of varieties of fish in single containers rather than the separate containers previously employed to prevent injury and death from vicious attacks upon one another or from wild thrashing about.

Unpublished results with MS-222 Sandoz

With the recent renewed interest in MS-222 Sandoz much work has been undertaken and most of it has been reported only in personal communications from the various investigators. This renewed interest was given impetus after Wood published that urethane, a drug previously used for fish anaesthesia, was found to cause cancer in laboratory mice after repeated doses. To protect fishery workers from any possibility of a similar reaction from their contact with the drug the use of MS-222 Sandoz as a possible replacement has been suggested.

In anaesthetizing game fish for easier handling, the need is for rapid anaesthesia of short duration and a rapid return of the fish to normal activity. In order to effect these requirements a fairly high concentration of MS-222 Sandoz is used, with relatively few fish passing through the solution at a time and an ample supply of fresh water on hand to receive them. The intensity of the effect of a given concentration varies inversely with the size of the fish. An increase in toxicity has been observed and correlated to a marked rise in temperature of the solution. Little difference has been observed among the various species, with the exception of some strains of rainbow trout which appear more sensitive to the drug.

In his study on Eastern Brook Trout (*Salvelinus fontinalis*), Ritzi observed the ability of fish to recover after all respiratory movements had ceased for several minutes. In these cases, time for recovery was quite long. This fact may account for some error in reported mortality figures. A wide range of satisfactory concentrations in relation to anaesthesia duration has been reported. An average ratio for 5-10 inch specimens at a temperature of from 40° to 60°F (5-15°C) is shown in Table III.

Allison reported on the hatching success of trout eggs artificially spawned by two different stations using MS-222 Sandoz. One station had good results; the other station's results were poor. After careful analysis of the results, Allison concluded that in order to obtain good results in spawning fish, using an anaesthetizing agent, it is advisable to take precaution against the possibility of the anaesthetizing solution's contacting reproductive products. This can be done easily by rinsing anaesthetized fish in fresh water before spawn is taken, and making certain that gloves or other objects do not carry the anaesthetizing solution to reproductive products.

Tests carried out by the Central Marine Fisheries Research Station of India showed that *Tilapia mossambica* weighing from 5-50 grams placed at 29°C in a 1:500 non-

TABLE III USE OF MS-222 SANDOZ IN SALMON, TROUT AND BASS

Variety of fish	Concentration	Anaesthesia time
Silver Salmon	0.5 to 1.0 Gm/US gal (1:7,600 to 1:3,800)	2 to 4 mins.
Sockeye Salmon	0.5 to 1.0 Gm/US gal (1:7,600 to 1:3,800)	2 to 4 mins.
Lake Trout	0.5 to 1.0 Gm/US gal (1:7,600 to 1:3,800)	2 to 4 mins.
Brown Trout	0.5 to 1.0 Gm/US gal (1:7,600 to 1:3,800)	2 to 4 mins.
Rainbow Trout	0.25 to 1.0 Gm/US gal (1:15,000 to 1:3,800)	1 to 2 mins.
Large Mouth Bass	0.5 to 1.0 Gm/US gal (1:7,600 to 1:3,800)	2 to 4 mins.
Small Mouth Bass	0.5 to 1.0 Gm/US gal (1:7,600 to 1:3,800)	2 to 4 mins.

aerated tap water solution of MS-222 Sandoz were anaesthetized immediately and later recovered rapidly. In aerated water under the same conditions the effects were the same except for the fact that the time needed for anaesthetization was longer.

The Hokkaido Salmon and Trout Hatchery Station in Japan carried out various field tests with MS-222 Sandoz. In tagging mature salmon *Oncorhynchus keta* (Walbaum) the investigators used 1:50,000 solutions of MS-22 in river water. Within a minute or a minute and a half the salmon were anaesthetized. After tagging they were returned to river water and recovered within several minutes.

MS-222 Sandoz in concentrations of 1:20,000 in sea water or salt water of low concentrations was used to anaesthetize rainbow trout so that they could be measured and weighed.

It is advisable that fish going on a lengthy journey should be starved beforehand. If they are fed preparatory to transportation then they are liable to choke if shaken up. On a very long trip some ice in the water will help to prevent the temperature from rising to their detriment.

Ova can be transported over long distances, but if they are rested for any length of time in transit (say, in excess of 12 hours) then it is advisable not to disturb them again until the eye has developed in the egg. The ova should be packed, not too tightly, between layers of wet moss.

THE ARTIFICIAL BREEDING OF COARSE FISH

Although this subject will be dealt with more fully in respect of individual species, a few brief notes here may help the reader who is contemplating some form of fish culture.

Spawn should be hatched as naturally as possible. It is best hatched in protective boxes, but for good results the fry should not be kept in confinement longer than necessary. Once the fry are hatched, the boxes should be placed in the 'nursery pool' and the young fish allowed to find their own way to freedom in this larger stretch of water.

A few freshwater shrimps are ideal for keeping a pond free of uneaten food.

Where possible a small separate pond should be reserved for feeding up inferior fish. Where the species are cannibalistic small fish will not survive if put in with larger ones. Likewise, fish kept too long in a nursery will take time to adjust to open water. Common sense must be used, but as a rough guide, bear in mind that fish should be released at the 'large minnow' stage.

GILL FEVER

Gill fever is one of the most common diseases. It is an inflammatory infection, similar to typhoid, and is most prevalent in young fish. The infected fish develops a small red spot on the thorax, and swims around erratically, gasping with the mouth open. Those that are lucky enough to survive produce abnormalities, but in most cases the fish die in infancy.

One of the causes of gill fever is the water being too shallow. A minimum depth of 4 feet prevents the disease, and is sometimes a cure if the infected fish are transferred soon enough.

FEEDING

The reader, having taken the trouble to ensure that his pool is suitable for the type of fish which he intends to breed, will fail abysmally if he neglects the subject of feeding. If fed properly, fish will grow quickly and maintain good health. It is a factor which is vital to success, and for this reason the author consulted Edward Baker Ltd, Cornard Mills, Sudbury, Suffolk, in order that the correct and most up-to-date information is given in this book, and they have kindly consented to information contained in their booklet on Omega Quality Fish Foods being reproduced here.

During the last decade, Edward Baker Ltd have manufactured by far the largest proportion of fish foods supplied to the developing fish farming industry in the U.K. Over this period, considerable manufacturing 'know how' has been built up, which has resulted in the installation of specialized machinery and the introduction of rigid quality control of raw materials and finished products. The same experienced personnel have been involved from the beginning, both with manufacture and marketing and with field testing of the products. With these facilities and background, they have introduced their new range of Trout and Salmon foods under their brand name "Omega".

There are feeds available for every need: floating, slow sinking and high density, depending upon the individual farmer's requirements. Details are given of each type in the appropriate chapters on the individual species.

All the diets are scientifically formulated and based on the most up-to-date research available. Close liaison is maintained with research institutes throughout the world.

The raw materials used in the foods are selected for quality and high digestibility in the fish. The system of quality control and design of the plant is such that unsatisfactory raw materials can be rejected. Correct mixing is 'policed' by an electronically controlled weighing system which has built-in safety devices.

With the advantages mentioned, and the close liaison between manufacturer and the fish farmer, Edward Baker Ltd are confident they can supply competitive high quality fish foods for every need.

Waders

A good pair of waders are essential. There are innumerable occasions when you will have to wade in your pond. In the case of ornamental garden ponds wellington boots may suffice for most of the time, but a sudden movement is inclined to create a wave and before you know it you have acquired a boot full of water! Waders are always useful. They are less cumbersome than waterproof trousers during wet weather and will keep your legs warm and dry when working outside around your pond. *Studded soles* are recommended. The bottoms of pools and ponds are generally slippery and studs will enable you to become more versatile in the water.

Aerators

An aerator is necessary for maintaining the required amount of oxygen in the water, and it will also help to prevent the water from freezing in the winter. A floating ½hp single phase, with a control box and 50 feet of submersible cable should be sufficient for the average fish-breeder. This size will aerate as much as 200 gallons per minute, and will cost about £300.

Transport Tanks

When we have prepared fish for transport by using tranquilizers, (see pp. 39—46), the basic fact remains that we need something to put them in. Fibreglass is an ideal substance from which these containers can be made, and should present no problem to the d-i-y enthusiast. As a guide, a useful, average size is approximately 2½ feet long by 2 feet wide and 1½ feet high. This will hold about 23 gallons of water.

It is important to bear in mind when making one of these that the easier it is to put fish in and get them out again, the less harm they are likely to suffer. On no account should empty polythene containers be put to use as fish transporter tanks. Apart from the unsuitability of size and shape of the average container, the neck is generally so narrow that fish will be damaged as a result.

Egg Equipment

An **egg-picker**, for the removal of 'dead' eggs as described in a later chapter, is simply a glass rod. An **egg tray** can easily be constructed of fibreglass, but remember that you will need a basket in which to carry it, as well as a screen to protect the eggs. The standard commercial tray is approximately 357mm in length, 39mm wide, and 17mm deep, weighing about 17kg.

Landing nets

These are a necessity. Fish need to be caught for a variety of reasons and it is important that this is carried out as easily as possible with little harm to the fish. The size of the mesh will depend upon the size of the fish which you breed. Nets and frames are sold separately, and the breeder will save himself money if he learns how to repair nets. Thick nylon twine can be purchased which is ideal for this purpose.

Protective netting

Fish must be protected at all times from predatory birds such as herons, and the amateur should be organised in this respect before putting fish in his pond. Thick nylon twine will serve admirably.

It is imperative that nets are kept in good repair when not in use. They should be folded to avoid tangling, and any holes repaired. It is time-wasting to leave repairs until the time when fish need to be caught up.

Feeders

Automatic feeders are essential to the amateur who is not able to hand-feed his fish at the appropriate times. It is no good throwing in an extra few handfuls before leaving for work, or asking a friend to do you a favour and feed your fish. Surplus food fouls the water, and even the best of friends are likely to forget!

A feeder can be purchased for about £30, which is fairly reasonable by today's prices. It is an investment that will repay you in terms of well-grown, healthy fish.

Weed Control

It may well be that the breeder has taken over an over-grown pond and wishes to develop it for fish culture. The first task will be to clear the weed. There are three ways in which this can be done:

1 By an application of specialized water-weed killer. This can be expensive if the volume of water is sizeable. Some years ago the author spent £15 in an attempt to clear a pond holding 10,000 gallons of water. The weed was algae, and although the particular substance, app-lied with a crop-sprayer, was effective, for some time afterwards dead weed was floating on the surface. Possi-bly method 3 would have been better in this case.

2 A weedcutter, costing upwards of £30. This consists of a series of 'V' shaped wire cutters with a chain attached at either end. It needs two persons to operate it, one stand-ing on either bank, dragging the cutters to and fro across the pool.

3 A 'drag', similar to the commercial weedcutter, can be made from a length of wire netting enclosed in a wooden frame and operated by two people in the same way (See Figure 6). Floating weed, such as algae, can be dragged to the banks and then scooped out of the water. It will be necessary, though, to drag the area several times because algae invariably dodges the netting, being carried beneath it and bobbing up again in its wake.

NOTES ON MAKING EQUIPMENT FROM FIBREGLASS

As we have already seen, it is possible to make some items of basic equipment out of fibreglass, namely transport tanks and egg trays.

Fibreglass is easy to work with. First, one must make a 'master', a mould made out of wood. The fibreglass is unrolled and smoothed so that it fits the master as closely as possible. Fibreglass matt is then poured on to it which sof-

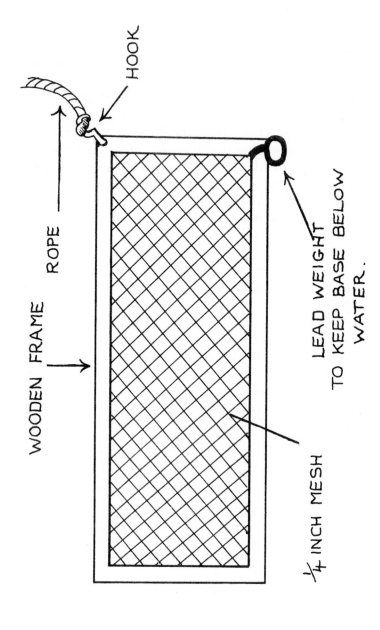

HOOK

ROPE

WOODEN FRAME

LEAD WEIGHT
TO KEEP BASE BELOW
WATER.

¼ INCH MESH

Figure 6 A weed drag.

Plate 4 Carp *(From painting by Jim Dunford.)*

tens it, and a tight 'fit' is possible.

Remember, **fibreglass is porous**. Unless it is treated with gel-coat, a type of waterproof paint, by the time your fish reach their destination the tanks will be dry and they will be dead; likewise, your eggs will be stranded on dry land.

Detailed instructions are usually supplied by most retailers who sell fibreglass, and the amateur is advised to heed these carefully. Having made your first batch of equipment, leave it filled with water for a few days to make sure that it really is waterproof.

Hen Salmon being stripped of her eggs.

4
TROUT BREEDING

Rows of immersed eggs under incubation.

CHAPTER FOUR

Trout Breeding

The author makes it clear at the outset that 'trout' includes Common, Rainbow, Moorland Stream, Golden and Brook. Whilst most fish-farms concentrate mainly on Common or Rainbow, the same methods of rearing may be applied to all the species.

First, though, let us examine some of the different species of trout which will concern the amateur fish-breeder.

BROWN (COMMON) TROUT

The body is about five times as long as it is deep. *All* the fins are soft-rayed. The dorsal fin has between 10 and 13 rays, the anal fin 9 or 10. It is golden brown in colour, with brown or black spots on its sides, back and dorsal fin, and a few red or orange spots along the lateral surface; the dorsal and adipose fins are spotted with bright orange or red. The belly is yellowish, but sometimes it is white on small trout which are born in streams. In young fish the tail is forked, but becomes square as they grow to maturity. The pectorals, ventrals, and anal fin are light brown without any markings. There are well-developed teeth in a zig-zag row on the vomer. Trout vary in size according to feeding and their environment.

RAINBOW TROUT

This fish has a thickset body, with black spots all over it, and red or purple bands along the flanks. During the spawning season the males are greyish-black with a rich mauve lustre, whilst the females are paler. The dorsal fin has 4 hard and 9 or 10 soft rays, the anal fin 3 hard and 10 or 11 soft. The lateral line comprises 120-150 small scales.

Rainbow trout are often bred in ponds together with carp, provided there is some running water, i.e. a stream going in and out of the pool. The female lays 500-3,000 eggs which she hides after fertilization in sand or gravel on the bed of the stream or pool. This species grows up to 5 inches in its first year. Whilst the average weight of a mature fish is 1-2½lb, they may weight anything up to 12lb according to feeding and environment.

The Rainbow Trout was brought to Europe from the United States of America in 1882.

GOLDEN TROUT

This fish is recognised by a carmine stripe in the middle of its side, with yellow on the lower side, rosy opercles, 10 parr marks, orange-tipped dorsal fin, white tipped anal and ventrals, spotted caudal, adipose and dorsal. The head and body are spotted to the lateral line, and the caudal peduncle is usually completely spotted.

Although the flesh of the Golden Trout is more oily than that of other trout, it is exceptionally good eating. However, to obtain the best flavour it should be smoked. (*See* Chapter Three).

BROOK TROUT

The Brook Trout has a flattened body, large elongated head with a deeply cleft mouth, and large eyes set above the entire centre line of the body. The dorsal fin contains 3-5 hard and 8-10 soft rays, the anal fin 3-5 hard and 7-9 soft. The lateral line numbers 109-130 scales, and the first branchial arch incorporates 11-22 gill-rakers. The basic colour of the fish is olive green, marbled on the back but breaking up into irregular yellow, orange, or red spots on the flanks.

58

The belly is usually silvery-mauve but sometimes it may be grey or even orange, or deep orange in mature males. The anal, ventral, and pectoral fins are red or orange with a black and white trim on the front edge. Males are more vividly coloured than females with a hook-shaped curvature of the lower maxillary bone.

The Brook Trout was imported to Europe from the United States of America in 1884, and spread to Britain from Germany. It likes cool, clean brooks and mountain streams, and will interbreed easily with the Brown Trout. The average mature fish weighs 1-2lb, and is 12-16 inches in length. It can also be kept in ponds if there is running water.

Pure running water is the vital essential in trout rearing. It should come from a river or stream as tap-water is usually fatal to these fish.

The temperature must not be liable to sudden changes, and the water should have a depth of not less than 4 feet. The current must not be strong.

If the reader owns, or has the use of, land on which the above requirements are to be found, then he is in an ideal position to begin trout breeding. **He should bear in mind, though, that to take or divert water from a stream requires a licence from the local Water Authority**. The author has obtained this on his own land and has to pay an annual licence fee of £10 for the privilege.

Until the breeder has gained some experience it is preferable to purchase 'fingerlings' (baby trout) from a reputable fish farm. Once the rudiments of rearing have been mastered then the hatching of ova can be experimented with.

As a guide to the amateur, the average fish-farm prices for Rainbow and Brown Trout are given on page 60.

HATCHING

In order to follow the process of trout breeding right through, it is proposed to begin with the actual hatching of

TABLE IV FISH-FARM PRICES FOR BROWN TROUT

Average length overall (inches)	Brown Trout		
	100	500	1,000
	£ p	£ p	£ p
2	9.00	43.00	81.00
3	10.00	47.50	90.00
4	12.00	57.00	108.00
5	16.00	76.00	144.00
6	21.50	102.00	193.00

TABLE V FISH-FARM PRICES FOR RAINBOW TROUT

Average length overall (inches)	Rainbow Trout		
	100	500	1,000
	£ p	£ p	£ p
2	8.00	37.00	70.00
3	9.00	42.00	79.00
4	10.50	49.00	93.00
5	14.00	66.00	125.00
6	19.00	90.00	170.00

TABLE VI FISH-FARM PRICES FOR OVA AND FRY

	1,000	5,000	10,000
	£ p	£ p	£ p
Eyed ova	6.00	—	46.00
Fry ready to feed (Mar/Apl)	13.00	62.00	—
Fry one month feeding (about May)	17.00	80.00	—

the ova, but the prospective breeder is advised to refer back to this part of the book once he has gained experience from the purchasing of fry onwards.

An outbuilding is suitable for use as a hatchery provided that it has ample lighting and is fairly roomy.

The hatching boxes should be placed in 2½-3 inches of

running water, and arranged in tiers, resembling a staircase. Perforated zinc is ideal for hatching ova on, with spouts of lead piping used for outlets. Light wooden covers will be needed to exclude the light from the eggs, and glass tubes are handy for moving the eggs and fry. If the thumb is pressed tightly over one end of one of these tubes, and then suddenly removed, water and eggs will automatically be sucked up. The eggs should be returned to the tray immediately after examination. Dead eggs can be removed with a pair of forceps.

SPAWNING

Those who spawn their own fish will need small flue or trammel nets to stretch across the spawning streams. Landing nets of the type sold by most angling shops will be sufficient to remove the fish from the water. The fish must be placed in containers. A separate can will be necessary to hold the eggs.

Obviously a percentage of fish which are caught in this way will not be spawning, and these can be released immediately after examination.

Trout go upstream to spawn once the cold weather sets in. Where possible these streams should be cleaned out prior to the spawning season, but sufficient weed should be left to act as cover. When searching a stream for trout always walk upstream so that the mud which discolours the water is swept away behind you.

Trout are easily sexed. The beginner will soon learn to feel the eggs in the fish, and ripe trout must be separated from the others. Males will be kept for fertilization, but remember that one male is capable of impregnating two or three females.

The process of taking eggs from a trout is relatively simple although it requires practice. The spawning pan is placed on the ground beside the person catching the trout. A female is caught and allowed to kick in the net for a few seconds to induce it to yield its eggs more easily. Hold the head gently with a piece of flannel, a companion keeping the fish extended by holding its tail. The trout should be held sideways with the vent as near to the bottom of the container as possible. The fish must then be 'stripped' with your free hand. Begin at the upper end of the ovary which extends nearly to the pectoral fin, and move the pressure quickly and gently to the vent. Avoid backward pressure which might injure the fish.

If a fish refused to yield all its eggs then it must be put into a separate container of fresh water for a few minutes and the process repeated. This method is invariably successful. After spawning, each fish must be returned to the water.

When one or two females have been 'stripped', the male must be held over the eggs and his sperm taken in exactly the same way. The container must be tilted so that the sperm mixes with the eggs, and then just enough water added so that the eggs are covered. After this has been done, the container must be set aside until all the eggs have separated, and then they are ready to pour into the spawning pan. They will at once sink to the bottom. The separation of the eggs usually takes about half-an-hour, and while this is happening other fish can be spawned.

When enough eggs have been collected and fertilized in the manner described, they must be taken back to the hatchery and distributed in the troughs, using a glass tube to do this; then water must be allowed to run over them. Fill the troughs from the lowest in the tier upwards so that the shells of the first hatched do not obstruct the eggs below them.

The eggs must remain in the hatching troughs until the eyes of the embryo are visible through the shell. A daily examination is vital, the dead ones being removed either with a glass tube or with a pair of forceps. A dead egg is white and opaque, easily discernible from the live ones. If they are left in the troughs a fungus will appear on them which will soon spread to the rest of the eggs.

The slower the eggs hatch, the healthier will be the fish. Nature herself caters for young fish between the age of four and eight weeks, depending on the temperature of the water, heat increasing and cold retarding the consumption of oil in the vesicle and controlling the development of the body.

Young fish require no food at all in the very early stages. It is easy to tell when they are beginning to need food by the way they dart at insects in the water. They can then be fed with finely chopped liver preparatory to giving them specialised foods, which will be dealt with later in this chapter.

Hatching, once the necessary experience has been gained, is, in fact, easier than rearing. The fry must now be transferred to feeding boxes, about 6 feet long by 15 inches wide, an area which is capable of holding 20,000 in the very early stages. Excess air in the water should be avoided at all costs, and the boxes must be kept clean. Feed little and often, and remove all uneaten food. Any weaker fry should be transferred to a separate box.

About July, when the fry are approximately 2 inches long, they are ready to be turned into a pond. The water should be around 60°F. Some breeders hang carrion over the water so that maggots drop into it, but with modern feeding methods this is not really necessary. Nevertheless, there is no harm in it.

Trout are usually turned out to stock rivers or pools at about a year old.

LAYOUT OF PONDS

As the reader becomes more experienced at breeding trout he will invariably wish to expand. This will entail digging out more ponds, something which must not be done haphazardly.

It is hoped that the diagram will enable him to make the best possible use of the water at his disposal. Remember, though, that the water must not be allowed to become stagnant. If the land is sloping then the task is that much easier

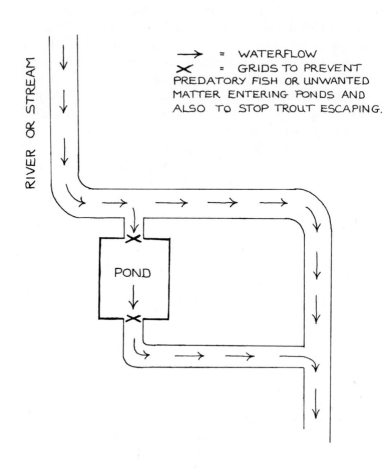

Figure 7 Small-scale fish breeding.

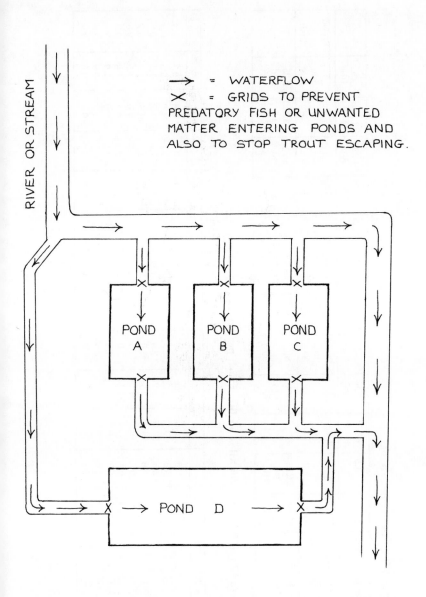

Figure 8 A fish-farm on a larger scale.

TABLE VII DAILY FEEDING GUIDE

Length of fish cm / in.	No. of fish per Kilo	No. of fish per lb.
-2.5 / -1	More than 5,000	More than 2,270
2.5-3.5 / 1-1.4	5,000 to 2,000	2,270 to 910
3.5-5 / 1.4-2	2,000 to 700	910 to 320
5-7.5 / 2-3	700 to 200	320 to 90
7.5-10 / 3-4	200 to 85	90 to 39
10-12.5 / 4-5	85 to 40	39 to 18
12.5-15 / 5-6	40 to 25	18 to 11.3
15-17.5 / 6-7	25 to 17	11.3 to 7.7
17.5-20 / 7-8	17 to 11	7.7 to 5
20-22.5 / 8-9	11 to 7.4	5 to 3.3
22.5-25 / 9-10	7.4 to 5	3.3 to 2.25
25 / 10+	5 and less	2.25 and less
Brood Fish		

Kilos (or lb) of Food per 100 Kilos (or lb) of Fish per Day

Length of fish	Water Temp 5°C	7	9	11	13	15	17	19	21
-2.5	3.0	3.4	4.0	4.8	5.6	6.4	6.7	3.8	2.9
2.5-3.5	2.8	3.3	3.8	4.6	5.4	6.1	6.5	3.6	2.7
3.5-5	2.6	3.1	3.6	4.4	5.1	5.9	6.3	3.5	2.5
5-7.5	2.3	2.7	3.2	3.7	4.3	5.1	5.3	2.8	2.2
7.5-10	1.9	2.3	2.6	3.0	3.5	4.0	4.3	2.5	1.9
10-12.5	1.6	1.8	2.1	2.4	2.7	3.2	3.5	1.9	1.5
12.5-15	1.4	1.6	1.9	2.1	2.5	2.8	3.0	1.7	1.3
15-17.5	1.2	1.4	1.6	1.9	2.2	2.5	2.6	1.5	1.1
17.5-20	1.0	1.2	1.4	1.6	1.9	2.2	2.3	1.2	0.9
20-22.5	0.9	1.1	1.3	1.5	1.7	2.0	2.1	1.1	0.8
22.5-25	0.8	1.0	1.2	1.4	1.6	1.9	2.0	1.0	0.7
25	0.7	0.9	1.1	1.3	1.5	1.8	1.9	0.9	0.6
Brood Fish	0.4	0.5	0.6	0.7	0.8	0.9	0.9	0.6	0.5

for the current can be induced to flow from one pond to another. However, if it is flat, then the water will have to be pumped through the individual pools.

Some natural food should always be available in the water, and many of the fish-farms today supply freshwater snails, shrimps, and caddis larvae.

FEEDING

Commercial foods have made fish-breding very much simpler than it was years ago. The author consulted Messrs. Edward Baker Ltd, of Cornard Mills, Sudbury, Suffolk, on this matter and the following information was kindly supplied by this firm in respect of their Omega Quality Fish Foods. Their Daily Feeding Guide and Ordering Guide will be invaluable to the beginner, ensuring that he does not overstock and consequently have surplus food left on his hands, nor overfeed or underfeed his growing trout.

TABLE VIII FOOD ORDERING GUIDE PER 10,000 TROUT

Fish size	Fish length cm (in.)	Quantity of food in bags	Approx. time to consume at 13-15°C water temperature
Fry "Fine Starter"	About 2.5cm. (-1")	½ kg.	4-8 days
Fry No. 0	2.5-3.75 (1-1+")	1 x 5 kg.	3-4 weeks
Fry No. 1	3.75-7.5 (1+"-3")	2 x 25 kg.	10-12 weeks
Fry No. 2	7.5-10 (3"-4")	3 x 25 kg.	6- 8 weeks
Fry No. 3	10-12.5 (4"-5")	6 x 25 kg.	6- 8 weeks
Trout No. 4	12.5-15 (5"-6")	10 x 25 kg.	6- 8 weeks
Trout No. 5	15-20 (6"-8")	20 x 25 kg.	10-12 weeks
Trout No. 6 (up to 230g (½ lb))	20-27.5 (8"-11")	80 x 25 kg.	10-12 weeks
Trout No. 6	27.5-30 (11"-12")	60 x 25 kg.	6- 8 weeks
Trout No. 6	30-32.5 (12"-13")	65 x 25 kg.	5- 7 weeks

Factors in Trout Feeding

From the Ordering Guide the approximate amounts to order and the time taken to consume the food are given, assuming the water temperature is 13°-14°C which is about optimum for maximum growth.

Having this information, and making allowances for varying water temperature and price, it is possible to calculate for budgeting purposes the approximate finance required for a group of fish.

The Daily Feeding Guide should be adhered to fairly closely, as overfeeding can affect the food conversion and cause overfatness. Underfeeding can also affect the food conversion and predispose the fish to stress.

In order that the correct amount can be fed, it is necessary to sample and weigh the fish fortnightly. Thus the weight of fish can be calculated in each pond and the appropriate amount of food given for the current water temperature. It is important to sample, as at fast-growing times of the year, e.g. spring, the weight increase each week in a pond is considerable. To obtain a representative sample, it is suggested that at least 100 fish are weighed from each group. With fry, 5% of the total should be sampled twice weekly, as the percentage weight increase is very much higher.

Trout that are to be marketed for the table can have the amount of food increased 25-30% above the Daily Feeding Guide recommendations during the last month. This will generally give a better conditioned fish. The extra food is best given by increasing the number of feeds so that the stomach is not overloaded at any one time.

Trout larger than 230g (1/2lb) should be fed according to condition and growth rate required. Use the column on the Daily Feeding Guide for 25cm (10 in) length fish as a starting point.

The supplementary feeding of fisheries over winter, or where natural food is limited, is a matter of judgement for the individual manager. However, it is usually about one-

Plate 7   Leather Carp (*Cyprinus carpio*) by B. Brooke-Smith

Plate 8 Perch *(From painting by Jim Dunford.)*

third to half the quantities recommended in the Daily Feeding Guide.

A high growth rate is generally achieved by feeding at regular intervals, especially during the fry stage, and an efficient automatic feeder is recommended. Good hand feeding with larger fish is still considered to give more control on the overall food conversion. Other advantages of hand feeding are that the food can be restricted on days when, for various reasons, the fish do not feed as heavily. The symptoms of disease can also be more easily detected. Well-adjusted Demand Feeders can also give these advantages.

In order that the right size of pellet can be fed, it is essential that the fish are 'graded', otherwise the size range in any group becomes too wide and cannibalism may take place, which can be the cause of unexplained losses. When changing food to the next size, it is advisable to mix in the new size gradually over a period of about 10-14 days.

Brown trout will normally consume about 15% less than Rainbow trout and can take up to double the time to obtain the same weight.

Pigmenting the flesh

Pigmentation of the flesh can be achieved by feeding the pigment (Canthaxanthin) in the food for 6-8 weeks before marketing or restocking. The intensity of pigmentation is dependent on many factors, but primarily on the intake of the food over the period and the level of pigment.

At lower water temperatures, therefore, pigmentation will take longer. It has been found that, when very high levels of pigment have been used for short periods, it is not deposited so firmly in the flesh and is more easily removed on cooking. Generally, for management reasons, it is recommended that the lower level is fed over a longer period.

When the pigment is withdrawn, the flesh will gradually lose its colour. Fish that are restocked into rivers and lakes will maintain their colour providing there is plenty of natural food available containing pigment, e.g. Gammarus, etc.

Medication

Medicated foods can be supplied for the treatment of bacterial diseases in fish, provided a veterinary prescription is obtained in the U.K. One tonne lots or over can be supplied, otherwise it is suggested that the antibacterial agent is added to the food on the farm at the time. It is recommended that diagnosis is carried out in conjunction with the veterinary profession.

Trout fry foods

Sizes available	Weight of fish (g.)	Length of fish (ins.)	Recommended no. of feeds daily
No. 0	-0.75	-1½	8-10
No. 1	0.75-5	1½-3	6-7
No. 2	5-11	3-4	5-6
No. 3	11-25	4-5	5-6

Physical Form Graded granules.

Application Intended to be fed to Rainbow Trout from the 'swim up' stage to about 25g (i.e. approx. 5in. in length). Contains a minimum amount of 'fines', thus reducing the possibility of gill problems. The protein and energy levels are high to give maximum growth at a wide range of water temperatures.

See Daily Feeding Guide for feeding rates.

Dispenses well from Automatic and Demand feeders. As it is important to obtain the best possible start, it is a false economy to use a cheaper lower quality diet at this stage, consequently Omega Trout Fry Foods contain only the highest quality ingredients available.

Other Salmonids that can be reared successfully on Omega Trout Fry Foods are Brown Trout, Brook Trout and Char. Some of the Cyprinids can also be grown on after being fed initially to a suitable size on natural foodstuffs. It is important that the particle size used is not too large with

TROUT BREEDING

Calculated Analysis

		No. 0 & 1	No. 2 & 3
Oil	%	10.0	10.0
Protein	%	54.0	50.0
Fibre	%	2.0	2.5
Ash	%	9.0	10.0
Moisture	%	8.0	8.0
Carbohydrate	%	17.0	20.5
(Nitrogen Free Extractives)			

Cyprinids in the early stages.

A 'Fine Starter' powdered food is available on request in small quantities. Some farmers prefer to feed this to the fish for a few days, especially if part of a group start feeding before the others.

Storage Keep in a cool dry store. Do not order more than 2-3 months' supply in advance, or use last year's food, as vitamin levels gradually deteriorate although an antioxidant is added. Surplus Fry Food can be dampened at the time of feeding and fed to larger fish in small quantities.

Pack 25kg nett weight multi-walled paper sack including two moisture barriers.

Trout food (floating type)

Sizes available	Weight of fish (g.)	Length of fish (ins.)	Recommended no. of feeds daily
No. 4	25-40	5-6	4-5
No. 5	40-90	6-8	3-4
No. 6	90+	8+	3-4
No. 6 Pigmented	90+	8+	3-4
No. 6 High Pigmented	90+	8+	3-4

Physical Form Low temperature expanded floating pellet. The No.4 size will only partially float due to its small size.

71

Application Omega Trout Food (Floating Type) is designed for the growing of Rainbow and Brown trout from 25g (5in. in length) until an appropriate size for restocking lakes and rivers or the table. The main uses are in the larger pond systems and the supplementary feeding of fisheries. It also has advantages where water conditions are cloudy and situations where it is difficult to gauge the amount of feed, e.g. thinly populated ponds. Another advantage is that wastage from incorrectly adjusted automatic and demand feeders and overfeeding by hand, can be more easily detected. It dispenses well from mechanical feeders. See Daily Feeding Guide for recommended feeding rates.

Calculated Analysis

		No. 4	No. 5 & 6
Oil	%	8.0	6.0
Protein	%	47.0	41.0
Fibre	%	4.5	4.5
Ash	%	10.0	10.5
Moisture	%	8.0	9.0
Carbohydrate	%	22.5	29.0

Nitrogen Free Extractives)

Storage Keep in a cool dry store. Do not order more than 2-3 months supply in advance.

Pack 25kg nett weight multi-walled paper sack with moisture barrier.

Trout Growers (Slow Sinking)

Sizes available	Weight of fish (g.)	Length of fish (ins.)	Recommended no. of feeds daily
No. 5	40-90	6-8	3-4
No. 6	90+	8+	3-4
No. 6 Pigmented	90+	8+	3-4
No. 6 High Pigmented	90+	8+	3-4

Physical Form Low temperature extruded pellet.

Application Omega Trout Growers Food (Slow Sinking) is designed for use in the intensive methods of trout culture, from 40g (6in. in length) until marketing. It is especially applicable in cage systems, as due to its being slow sinking, less food is lost through the bottom of the cage. It dispenses well from mechanical feeders and has a low 'fines' content. See Daily Feeding Guide for recommended feeding rates.

Calculated Analysis

Oil	%	7.0
Protein	%	45.0
Fibre	%	4.5
Ash	%	12.0
Moisture	%	9.0
Carbohydrate	%	22.5
(Nitrogen Free Extractives)		

Storage Keep in a cool dry store. Do not order more than 2-3 months supply in advance.

Trout Food (High Density)

Sizes available	Weight of fish (g.)	Length of fish (ins.)	Recommended no. of feeds daily
No. 4	25-40	5-6	4-5
No. 5	40-90	6-8	3-4
No. 6	90+	8+	3-4
No. 6 Pigmented	90+	8+	3-4
No. 6 High	90+	8+	3-4

Physical Form Compressed compounded pellet.
Application Omega Trout Food (High Density) is intended

for use in the intensive systems where maximum growth and a low feed conversion is of paramount importance. Providing environmental conditions are favourable, a feed conversion ratio as low as 1.1 : 1 can be achieved. All the ingredients used in these high energy foods are the best available, hence the price per tonne is somewhat higher than other foods on the market. However, due to the very low food conversion ration, the food cost per pound (or kg) of trout produced will be lower, this being the most important single economic factor in trout production. The food is manufactured as a compressed compounded pellet on specially installed manufacturing machinery.

Calculated Analysis

		No. 4	No. 5 & 6
Oil	%	8.0	8.0
Protein	%	49.0	47.0
Fibre	%	3.0	4.5
Ash	%	11.0	10.0
Moisture	%	10.0	11.0
Carbohydrate (Nitrogen Free Extractives)	%	19.0	19.5

Storage Keep in a cool dry store. Do not order more than 2-3 months supply in advance.
Pack 25kg nett weight multi-walled paper sack with moisture barrier.

Trout Holding Food (Slow Sinking)

Size available	Weight of fish (g.)	Length of fish (ins.)	Recommended no. of feeds daily
No. 6	90+	8+	1-2

Physical Form Low temperature extruded pellet.

Application Omega Trout Holding Food is intended for situations where a slower growth rate is required for marketing reasons. This usually applies in the re-stocking market. This is where the farmer does not wish his fish to become too large too soon. There is less risk of the fish running into disease problems through scavenging on the bottom of ponds, cannibalism and stress, than feeding small quantities of the normal high performance diets. Feeding recommendations would be approximately 75% of levels on the Daily Feeding Guide. Do not feed high levels to trout over long periods, or in demand feeders. It is water stable, and is a suitable diet for Carp and other coarse fish in semi-intensive conditions.

Calculated Analysis

Oil	%	5.0
Protein	%	35.0
Fibre	%	5.5
Ash	%	10.5
Moisture	%	9.0
Carbohydrate (Nitrogen Free Extractives)	%	35.0

Storage Keep in cool dry store. Do not order more than 2-3 months supply in advance.

Brood Fish Food (Floating Type)

Size available	Weight of fish (g.)	Length of fish (ins.)	Recommended no. of feeds daily
No. 7	400+	12+	1-2

Physical Form Low temperature floating expanded pellet.
Application Omega Brood Fish Food is for feeding to selected Brown or Rainbow Trout and should be fed

throughout the year. The quantity to feed must be judged by the condition of the fish. It is important that they do not become overfat. The quantity fed is approximately half that for table-sized trout as indicated in the Daily Feeding Guide. Considerably higher levels of vitamins and other nutrients are included to compensate for the lower feeding rate, and to ensure adequate carryover of nutrients into the eggs. Pigment is included as it colours the egg, thus helping egg picking by hand or machine. It is also claimed to improve fertility and hatchability, although this has not been fully substantiated by research. Many factors can influence hatching results. It would appear with Rainbow Trout that if they are kept in water teperatures below 12°C during the summer months, hatchability and fertility are improved.

Calculated Analysis

Oil	%	7.0
Protein	%	50.0
Fibre	%	3.5
Ash	%	10.5
Moisture	%	9.0
Carbohydrate	%	20.0

(Nitrogen Free Extractives)

Storage Keep in cool dry store. Do not order more than 2-3 months supply in advance.
Pack 25kg nett weight multi-walled paper sack with moisture barrier.

Commercially, trout are probably the most lucrative of all fish to breed with the exception of salmon. Large numbers are constantly in demand for the re-stocking of rivers as well as being a popular food in most hotels and restaurants.

It should be noted by the reader, however, once he attains the status of commercial fish-farming, that under the Sal-

76

mon and Freshwater Fisheries Act 1972 written permission from the River Authority concerned is required for any stocking in their area, and the vendor should ensure that this has been obtained before unloading fish into any river.

Grading Parr.

5

SALMON

Parr in Tank.

Working at a fry tank.

CHAPTER FIVE

Salmon

ATLANTIC SALMON

The Atlantic Salmon has a torpedo-shaped body and resembles the Sea Trout in appearance. The dorsal fin has 3-5 hard, and 9-12 soft rays, the anal fin 3-4 hard and 7-10 soft. The lateral line has 114-130 small scales, and the first branchial arch has 17-24 gill-rakers. The caudal fin is forked. The flanks below the lateral line sometimes have black spots, and in some fish have none at all. While the salmon lives in the sea it is a silvery-blue colour, but it becomes darker during the spawning season. During this time the male is a reddish-brown colour with red spots appearing among the black ones. The lower jaw of the male elongates, curving upwards, but there are no such changes in the female.

The colour of the young before they leave the hatching area for the sea is similar to that of the trout, with 18-23 transverse spots on the body. During its journey back downstream the salmon is a silvery colour.

The mature salmon lives in the sea although it is hatched in fresh water, and remains in the river for sometime afterwards.

SPAWNING

The smaller specimens start upstream at the end of spring, but the larger ones do not follow until the end of summer or the beginning of autumn. The first lot spawn in

81

the autumn of the year of their arrival, but the later ones remain in the river during the winter and spawn in the following summer. On its journey up river the salmon does not feed, and is capable of jumping obstacles in excess of 10 feet high.

An adult female salmon is capable of laying up to 27,000 eggs, about half of which remain unfertilized. They spawn on gravelly or stony river beds, the female making a nest with her tail. They spawn only once or twice during their lives, and many die after spawning.

Usually the males return to the rivers after a couple of years at sea. They grow rapidly in the sea, and are capable of attaining 3 feet in 3 months. Some remain in the rivers all their lives, but their growth is slower.

The average maximum weight of the salmon is 85lb with a length of about 5 feet.

SALMON REARING

Salmon rearing is very similar to trout breeding. Indeed, the beginner could succeed by following the instructions contained in Chapter Four of this book. Young salmon are known as 'smolts'.

However, in order that the reader may realise the extent of the salmon industry throughout the world let us briefly take a look at what is known as **Salmon Ranching.**

Basically, a salmon ranch treats water and raises salmon. At the OreAqua Ranch on the Yaguina River estuary at Newport, Oregon, USA, there has been a tremendous expansion in the business lately. Forty million gallons of water per day are treated with chlorine, and then pumped into the ponds. This water is treated for dechlorination in a 'maze' pond, and the neutralised water is then ready for use.

Eggs are stacked in screen trays set in the ponds, and in these they will hatch and grow into smolts. All the feeders are automatic, and the water temperature can be controlled either to extend or to delay incubation. Young salmon usually double their weight within a month of hatching.

Salmon rearing is also practised in the USSR. Soviet experiments show that pink salmon fry easily adapt from fresh to salt water. A large fish farm on the Samur River is hoping to breed in the region of fifteen million salmon per annum, and there are plans to use warm water from nearby thermal power stations.

Cynrig Salmon Hatchery
(reproduced from C.E.G.B. booklet)

The hatchery is on the River Cynrig, an Usk tributary, and is run as part of the Scientific Services Department of the South Western Region of the Central Electricity Generating Board. It is the only salmon hatchery in the country run by the elec-tricity supply industry.

HISTORY

The salmon hatchery was opened in 1965 because of the effects of the two riverside power stations at Uskmouth, near Newport, on salmon migration to the open sea during April and May each year.

When the 'A' power station started generating in 1952 sal-mon in the River Usk were drawn through the cooling-water intakes. Fortunately, these fish could be rescued quite easily by netting and were returned to the river. However, when the 'B' station opened in 1961 the design of the cooling system in this larger station made fish rescue more difficult. Because of this, the two cooling water systems were inter-connected, at considerable cost, to enable both power stations to obtain river water through the older 'A' station intakes during the salmon migration. In this way, the hazards to fish were reduced and the efficiency of rescue operations improved.

In addition to the above modifications, the Board esta-blished the hatchery on the River Cynrig, an Usk tributary 60 miles upstream from Uskmouth, to rear young salmon for release as two-year-old smolts into the River Usk system.

Initially, these smolts were reared to compensate for losses caused by river water abstraction at Uskmouth power station. Because of the efficiency of the rescue operations, these losses have been negligible for several years, so the released smolts now make a worthwhile contribution to stocks in the river. Originally each fish was released with a numbered tag attached to facilitate identification if caught. From the information on numbers and location of fish recaptured in recent years, it has been possible to deduce the migrating movements of salmon released from the hatchery. It appears that these fish leave Cynrig and the Usk River and move down the Bristol Channel, around the southern and northern coasts of Ireland, and finally cross to the west coast of Greenland. They remain off Greenland for a year or two and return to the Cynrig area to spawn after completing a round trip of some 4,500 miles. Any surviving fish then return to the sea for another migratory cycle.

Much remains unknown about the salmon, and the hatchery is helping to fill some of the gaps in scientific knowledge.

The hatchery building contains offices, a laboratory, stores, food preparation and hatchery sections and a visitors' reception centre that can seat 40 people.

Outside equipment includes a series of tanks and ponds to accommodate the fish in their various stages of development.

Life cycle

The stages of the salmon's life cycle are:
1, Eggs; 2, Alevins; 3, Fry; 4, Parr; 5, Smolt.

It is as a smolt that the young salmon migrates to sea. After about 18 months it returns for the first time to its home river system for spawning. Later, the weakened fish, called a kelt, starts its downstream journey.

The maximum capacity of the hatchery is 250,000 eggs, out of which only 50,000 can be taken through to the fry stage. Some of the remainder die but the majority are given to the Usk River Division.

SALMON

First Year

In the first year the fish progress from the indoor incubator tanks to the outdoor deep fry tanks and then into the larger swedish fry tanks. The second year is spent in the round parr ponds.

Electro-fishing

The first stage of the hatchery's operation is to get the eggs. This is done in the spawning period in the middle of November when about 50 hens and fewer cock salmon are caught by electro-fishing in the Usk's smaller tributaries. Eggs are often also bought from a Scottish salmon hatchery.

The fish are attracted by a small electric current from an electrode in the water. This stuns them and they float downstream into a catch net. In the few hours before the hen recovers and is replaced in the river, her eggs are milked into a bucket.

The cock's milt is stripped on top of the eggs and river water added to make conditions as natural as possible.

Within seconds of mixing all the eggs are fertilised and excess dead milt can be washed off. After 30 minutes the eggs are strong enough to survive the road journey back to the hatchery, where they are placed 5,000 at a time in 50 indoor incubator trays.

Incubation

The time in the trays depends on the natural temperature of the filtered river water, which can vary from 0°C up to a winter maximum of 11°C. The norm is 80 days for hatching, with another six weeks for the alevins' yolk-sac to be absorbed.

Fry tanks

The fish are then moved outside and divided into two of the four deep fry tanks where feeding starts. By this time three per cent of the eggs have usually died.

Once every hour of daylight the fry are fed on raw liver until the day when growth stops due to the cramped conditions in the concrete tanks.

85

The fish in both tanks are then divided into all four containers to allow further growth.

In the first few weeks of this stage more than 10 per cent of the fish, now about three centimetres long, can die due to natural causes.

Swedish tanks

The fry are then transferred into the two-metre-square swedish tanks. The long and tedious task of individually counting the fry is now carried out so that the number in each tank is known. This job takes several days and is done only in cool weather or during the evening, as these conditions best suit the fish.

Initially, there are up to 10,000 fish in each tank but, as growth takes place, they are thinned out into adjoining tanks. By March there could be as few as 2,000 in each unit. The fatality rate by then has dropped to two per cent of the fry originally placed in the tanks.

Continual size grading helps stop cannibalism by keeping the stronger and faster-growing fish together. It is done with a special riddle so that the fry grade themselves according to girth.

Second Year

The final move takes place in March. With the two-year-olds being released into the river, the empty nine-metre-diameter concrete parr ponds are now ready to receive the next generation of one-year-olds.

The fry are graded into three sizes — one for each of the gravity-fed ponds. Now called parr, they range from 10 to 15 centimetres long and, by judicious feeding, are encouraged not to grow above 20 centimetres before release.

Depending on the weather, the parr are fed on high-protein pellets four times a day and, for good health, not more than 5,000 fish are kept in each tank.

After two years the smolt are placed into the Usk river system. About 10,000 fish a year are released.

SALMON

Water Supply

Fish require water of the right quality and temperature range. As the temperature depends on that of the river water, the hatchery is concerned mostly with maintaining the correct levels of dissolved oxygen and suspended solids. Quality is best ensured by a constant supply of fresh aerated water. If the flow were cut off completely, the parr could live in the tanks for about one day, but the fry could not survive for more than 60 minutes.

Diet

Various methods are used for feeding artificially-reared fish. Minced liver and pelleted protein are used at the hatchery, according to the age group being fed.

Hand-feeding is preferred to automatic devices as the colder the day the less the fish eat. An automatic feeder could not take this into account.

Tagging

In the years when tagging takes place each fish is given an individual tag number. After the smolt is anaesthetised, the tag is attached by two nylon threads just below the dorsal fin.

As well as a number, the address of the Ministry of Agriculture, Fisheries and Food is given, with the offer of a reward for the return of the tag if the fish is caught on its way back upstream.

It is hoped that fishermen or anglers who subsequently catch the reared fish will return the tags, which give valuable information on migratory movements of salmon, thus providing a basis for deciding on the best way of stocking rivers. Tagging used to be done every year, but is now done every three years as a composite picture of where the fish go has been compiled. The next taggings will be in the spring of 1981.

Although the principle of salmon rearing is virtually identical to that of raising trout, the beginner must study the subject of feeding very carefully, for here lies the key to success. In the sea the salmon feeds mostly on herrings, small fish, molluscs, and puts on as much weight as 11lb in a year, sometimes covering a hundred miles in a couple of weeks in search of food.

Artificially-developed foods will assist the amateur breeder in giving his salmon the correct diet, and so producing healthy fish for which there is a constant demand. Edward Baker Ltd of Sudbury, Suffolk, are able to supply the needs of the salmon rearer in this respect.

Salmon Starter Food

Sizes available	Weight of fish (g.)	Length of fish (ins.)	Recommended no. of feeds daily
No. 0	-0.3	-1¼	8-10
No. 1	0.3-5	1¼-3	6-7
No. 2	5-11	3-4	5-6
No. 3	11-25	4-5	5-6
No. 4	25-40	5-6	4-5

Physical Form Graded granules coated with oil. No. 4 — 2mm compressed compounded pellet.
Application Omega Salmon Starter Food is intended for feeding to Atlantic Salmon from hatching until smoltification at one or two years of age, when they are either released into a river system or adapted to sea water and grown on for table production. The proportion of one year old smolts is dependent mainly upon management, water temperature and strain.Raising the water temperature in the early stages has been shown, by research, to improve the economics of the freshwater phase. The successful rearing of salmon is

very dependent upon the first feeding period. The correct
presentation of the food, water depth and flow conditions,
as well as regular feeding at intervals with automatic feeders, are all necessary to avoid high mortalities from starva-
tion. It is suggested that operators who have not reared
salmon before seek advice. This food has a high oil content,
which has been shown experimentally to considerably
increase growth rate and reduce mortality during the first
year. Feeding rates for salmon are generally about 25% less
than those indicated on the Daily Feeding Guide, except during the first two months when feeding rates should be similar to those indicated on the Guide. Sizes No. 3 and No. 4 can
be fed in either freshwater or seawater.

Calculated Analysis

Oil	%	17.0
Protein	%	54.0
Fibre	%	2.0
Ash	%	12.0
Moisture	%	8.0
Carbohydrate	%	7.0
(Nitrogen Free Extractives)		

Storage Keep in a cool dry store. Do not order more than 2-3
months supply in advance. **Do not use last year's food.**
Pack 25kg nett weight multi-walled paper sack with external and internal moisture barrier.

Sea Salmon Food (High Density)

Physical Form Compounded compressed pellet, coated
with oil.
Application Omega Sea Salmon Food (High Density) is
intended for feeding to Atlantic Salmon being produced in
seawater for the table market. It is fed from the time the fish
are large enough to take the No.5 pellet during the first sum-

Sizes available	Weight of fish (g.)	Length of fish (ins.)	Recommended no. of feeds daily
No. 5			
	40-90	6-8	3-4
No. 5 Pigmented			
No. 6			
	90-200	8-10	3-4
No. 6 Pigmented			
No. 7			
	200+	10+	2-3
No. 7 Pigmented			

mer, until marketing as Grilse at about one year in the sea, or Salmon after about two years in the sea. Salmon do not feed as ravenously as Rainbow Trout and it is, therefore, important to encourage maximum intake by using automatic feeders or frequent hand feeding, especially during the first summer in the sea.

All sizes of Omega Sea Salmon Food are available with and without pigment; there being some evidence that there may be some benefit from feeding pigment (Astaxanthin and Canthaxanthin) throughout the seawater phase. Although some farmers, for economic reasons only, introduce the pigmented foods during the last 4-5 months. The onset of sexual maturity drastically reduces the colour of the flesh and growth rate, therefore it is important to market the fish before this occurs and also select a strain of fish which is late maturing. Daily feeding rates will be between 1-2% of bodyweight depending on the seawater temperature which is usually between 6-14°C.

Storage Keep in a cool dry store. Do not order more than 2-3 months supply in advance.

Pack 25kg nett weight multi-walled paper sack with external and internal moisture barrier.

Calculated Analysis

Oil	%	14.0
Protein	%	46.0
Fibre	%	3.5
Ash	%	9.0
Moisture	%	9.0
Carbohydrate	%	18.5
(Nitrogen Free Extractives)		

SALMON FISHING

Mostly salmon are caught near to estuaries as they make their way up river to spawn. Apart from the highly organised poaching which is detrimental to the salmon population of the world, there is another aspect of this illegal taking of salmon, on a much smaller scale but equally detestable. Salmon roe is ideal as bait for smaller fish, and often poachers will gaff salmon for this alone. A small jar of this roe will sell for as much as £5, and one salmon may yield up to eight or ten jars, a price which is in excess of the food value. Often local village poachers will kill salmon for their roe, throwing the carcase away in case they should be apprehended by the law on their way home.

Haaf-Netting

Although it is not intended in this book to cover angling, the subject of haaf-netting is unique, and it is felt that the chapter on salmon would be incomplete without some mention of this type of salmon-fishing.

Standing in the shadow of Criffel, on the west coast of Scotland, is the picturesque village of Glencaple. It is neat and tidy, its rows of terraced cottages each vying with its neighbour for an appearance of cleanliness and homeliness. The Nith Hotel is the most impressive building by far, standing on the estuary of that river, a large and majestic-looking building which seems to command the surrounding salt-

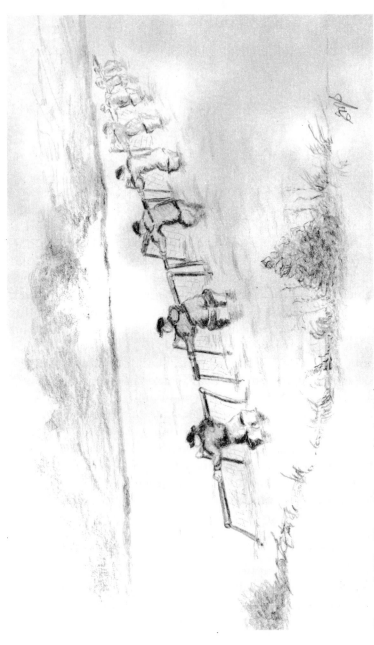

Figure 9 The Haaf Netters of the Solway Firth.

marshes as a monarch would survey his kingdom. One could not imagine a more peaceful setting when the weather is calm, or such desolation when the storm clouds gather and the gales howl across the Solway Firth. Such tranquility coupled with harshness live together, for here the weather may change within a matter of hours. The saltings, too, are treacherous, offering a firm foothold one day, only to be replaced by shifting quicksands the next. Many lives have been lost here over the centuries, for this is no place for the unwary. The swiftly flowing Solway tide comes in faster than a man can run, and few have lived to tell the tale of a race won back to the safety of the green merse when caught out on the vast mudflats.

Yet the inhabitants of Glencaple are a happy people, living from day to day, content with their lot, and asking nothing more of life. They are more prosperous today than ever before, many of them possessing transport which enables them to take more highly paid jobs in nearby Dumfries, or perhaps even Annan. However, it has not always been like this, and at one time many of the families living in this small village relied entirely upon the proceeds from their season's 'haaf-netting' to keep them from one year until the next.

Haaf-netting is a type of fishing which is unique to the Solway Firth, and nowhere else in the world do we meet up with it. The only clue we have which gives us cause to think that it may not have originated here is the word 'haaf'. 'Haaf' is Norse for sea, so possibly this method was introduced from Scandinavia, although we have no other proof to support this.

A 'haaf' is a pock-net, tied to a frame consisting of a beam 12-13 feet long, with three small sticks or rungs fixed into it, one in the centre and one at either end. These sticks are usually no more than 4 feet in length. The net is attached to these by a stout line. The fisherman will stand with the mouth of the net towards the current of the water, the points of the sticks firmly fixed to the bottom, holding the middle of the beam. The moment a fish swims into it, he must haul up the mouth of the net by means of the centre rung. The fish is now trapped in the pock, and he must despatch it as quickly as possible and prepare for the next one.

The 'centre' rung, in actual fact, is situated slightly to the right, and goes through the beam to form a handle. The haaf-netter must stand chest high in the incoming tide, his left hand on the middle of the beam, grasping the handle with his right, pushing the beam out to arm's length, and bracing himself firmly. The most important factor is to ensure that he maintains a firm foothold throughout.

The handle is pulled sharply back the moment he feels a fish strike his net, thereby rotating the beam on its axis, raising the rungs and the mouth of the net well clear of the water. Nowadays, chest-length waders are worn for this arduous occupation which requires no small amount of physical endurance, but over the centuries such improvisations as pieces of sailcloth were used. The women used to assist their menfolk, standing alongside them, despatching the fish as they were caught and putting them into bags.

Lots were cast for positions amongst the fishermen, up until a few years ago, when a large majority of the Solway people used to make their livelihood in this way. This means of determining their various stances were known as 'mells' and the winner had first choice of a place in which to set up his net. In order to conduct this in a fair manner, each man was required to build a small sand-castle on the shore. This completed, a person was called upon who had not watched the building, and he was required to kick the castles over one by one, thus determining the order in which their builders lined out across the estuary. Often a line consisted of a dozen or more men.

The batons used for killing the fish once they had been caught were also known as 'mells'. A sharp blow from one of these is usually sufficient to despatch the fish, there being a knack in the manner in which this is carried out, but the most important factor of all is to place the dead fish in the container without moving one's position. This is often difficult when the tide is flowing swiftly, and a slip could mean the loss of a valuable catch, or possibly worse.

The man on the outside of the line continues to fish until the water becomes too deep, when he will make his way shorewards at the rear of his colleagues. He is followed by the one standing next to him, and this goes on until all are standing on dry land. Once the tide begins to ebb, they wade out again in the same order, taking up their former positions again.

There always have been, and still are, a number of 'loners', men who prefer to haaf-net in solitude, taking up positions well away from their fellow men. Often these solitary fishermen are very experienced, not wishing to amalgamate their skills with those of less experienced fishers.

The rewards of this mode of living vary according to the supply of and demand for the fish. Many years ago the fish-buyers used to travel from the surrounding towns daily, in order to await the catches. Salmon varied from 3d to 1/- per lb, according to scarcity. The prices of herrings and sea-trout were much lower.

The haaf-netter must also take into consideration the price of his equipment. In olden days he would knit his own nets, but today these are mostly purchased, costing possibly £5 each. At least two nets will be required for a season's fishing. A wise fisherman will discard his net before it has rotted or broken, not risking the loss of a catch through false economy.

Nowadays, a permit is required before one is able to fish in the Caerlaverock area. However, this has not always been the case, for legend has it that the fishing rights were given to the locals by the Lords of Nithsdale as a reward for bravery shown in a lengthy siege of the castle. However, this custom has crumbled along with the structure of this historic building.

95

These hardy Solway people had other methods of catching their fish, long before the first haaf-net was ever thought of. One of these was known as fishing with 'leifters'. A leifter is a four-pronged fork with a 24-foot handle. The fisherman would patiently wait alongside the banks of a tidal river such as the Nith, and indiscriminately stab at schools of fish as they passed below him. There was not a great deal of skill attached to this, and often a number of fish were unnecessarily wounded.

Another old method is known as 'pock-net' fishing. This is carried out by fixing stakes in the sand at low tide, leaving the stakes about 3½ to 4 feet apart. A net is then tied between each stake, the underpart of this being made fast to a ring which is slipped over one of the stakes. The mouths of the nets are about 3 feet square. Fish become caught in these, and remain there for collection when the tide ebbs. There were strict rules governing this. Five pock-nets were known as a 'clout' and no man was allowed to have more than ten clouts set at any one time. He was also required to keep well away from the next fisherman.

In 'raise-net' fishing the lower part of the net floated on an incoming tide, but then settled down with the ebb to form a type of trap. These had to be set in the hollow parts of a tideway, and were of no use in either river channels or on open sands. Stakes measuring 12 feet in length were set in rows 6 feet apart, across the mouth of a hollow. A strong rope was fixed to the head of each stake, and a 10-foot net was tied to these, bound at the bottom with rope, but not attached to the stakes. Midway between each stake was a 12-foot long stick, fastened to the upper rope. The other end of the stick was secured to the bottom rope of the net, thereby keeping it stretched to its full width, whilst the lower ends floated, opening in the manner of a trap door and allowing the fish to enter. If the hollow or lake did not empty itself when the tide ebbed it was dragged with another net. Using this method it was possible to catch salmon, sea-trout, herring, sturgeon, cod and flounders.

Leifter, pock-net, and raise-net fishing have all become lost in the past. Stake-nets are still used in the estuaries to catch flounders, but salmon fishing is mostly confined to the shores of the Solway. Occasionally boats operate drift-nets out in the Firth, but even this is dying out.

Haaf-netting is still carried out in the same way as it was centuries ago. Little has changed in the actual mode of the fishing. Only the people have changed. They regard it not as a means of making a living, but a way in which to earn some extra cash. Some of the locals take an indoor job during the winter months, and then resort to haaf-netting during the summer. Within the last few years there was an attempt made to make this age-old method of fishing illegal. The argument against it was that too many salmon were being caught in this way as they made their way to their spawning grounds. In view of the other ways in which salmon are taken, including wholesale poaching, it would be a tragedy if these Scottish haaf-netters were deprived of an age-old tradition.

6
CARP

Crucian Carp

Plate 10 Bleak *(From painting by Jim Dunford.)*

CHAPTER SIX

Carp

Although we shall look at the different varieties of carp in this chapter, it must be borne in mind that, with regard to rearing, there is little or no variation in the procedure for each, and the term "carp" incorporates Crucian Carp, Mirror Carp, Leather Carp, and Silver Carp.

COMMON CARP

The Common Carp has a small mouth, no apparent teeth, and has a barbule or cirrus on the upper part of each corner of the mouth with a second smaller one above it on each side. The nostrils are large and the eyes are small, and the operculum is marked with striae radiating from the anterior edge, the nape and back rising sharply. The tail is forked, and the whole body is covered with large scales, about a dozen rows between the ventral and dorsal fins. The general colour is olive brown, the head being the darkest part. The belly is a yellowish white, the irides golden, and the fins are dark brown.

This fish was supposedly introduced to England by Leonard Mascall, but there are records of it being in England centuries ago. In the Privy Purse expenses of King Henry VIII in 1532 various entries are made of rewards being given to persons for bringing 'Carpes to the King'. Carp are also mentioned in the *Boke of St. Albans* printed in 1496.

In olden times monks ate Carp because they were necessary for the fasts instituted by the Roman Catholic religion, and they fetched an even higher price than salmon. The carp's popularity on the table waned during the twentieth century in England, but now it is reviving steadily, and one cannot help but wonder whether in the future it may figure prominently on the menu in hotels and restaurants. Certainly it is very popular in Germany. It is in season for the table between October and April.

Carp are very prolific breeders and are to be found in most large pools, lakes, canals, and sluggish rivers. They do not like a strong current. Strangely, there are few carp in Scotland.

Spawning

They being to spawn towards the end of May or in early June. The ova are deposited upon weeds in the bottom of the pool or on the river bed, the female being closely followed by two or three males. Once 600,000 ova were found in the roe of a 9lb female.

There is no evidence that the carp preys on other fish or their spawn. They eat little or nothing during winter, and for the remainder of the year their natural food is the larvae of insects, worms, and parts of aquatic plants. They attain 3lb in weight by their sixth year, and 6lb before their tenth. The adults vary from 12-30 inches in length and average 10-15lbs in weight. One was once caught on the Earl of Bradford's Estate at Weston-under-Lizard, Staffordshire, weighing 19½lbs. They are bred for ornamental purposes also.

CRUCIAN CARP

The head is obtuse, mouth and eyes small, the body short and thick, and the scales large. There are seven scales in an oblique line between the base of the first dorsal fin-ray and the tubular scale of the lateral line, with six scales below that and the origin of the ventral fin. The tail is forked, and divided into two almost equal rounded halves. The top of the head and the back are olive brown, the sides lighter in colour, the belly almost white, and the whole fish shines with a brilliant metallic lustre. Cheeks and gill-covers are bright golden yellow, the irides golden, the dorsal fin and upper part of the tail brown, tinged with orange. The pectoral, ventral and anal fins, and the lower part of the tail are deep orange.

The Crucian Carp was supposedly introduced into Portugal from the East Indies, from whence it spread to the rest of Europe. It is found all over Europe, Spain, southern Italy, and northern Finland. It was introduced into Britain about the middle of the eighteenth century, about the same time as the goldfish which was first kept in this country just prior to 1730. There is a possibility that the Crucian Carp was mistakenly imported with a batch of goldfish. Some believe that it is, in fact, a feral goldfish.

The Crucian Carp first established itself in the River Thames, and from there it spread to East Anglia and the Midlands. Seldom is it found in Ireland or Scotland. The building of networks of canals after the Industrial Revolution could well have been responsible for its distribution throughout England. Certainly this species is well suited to this type of water, being very fond of clay soils and not liking strong currents.

Breeding

Mating takes place between either a pair or three fish, and spawning occurs about the end of April or early May. The eggs are small and numerous, and having little yolk they hatch quickly into small fry, remaining in the weeds and feeding on algae and other plant life.

Crucian Carp move in shoals, foraging for food by both day and night. They will split up if common carp inhabit the same water, but generally congregate again after dark. Usually the Crucian feeds only in summer, although it is resistant to winter temperatures and survives well below the ice in a frozen pool. It is also able to exist for long periods in the mud of a dried-up pond during severe droughts.

Crucian Carp are bottom-feeding fish, but will readily take floating foods and baits. They are capable of living 25-30 years, but a fish over 2lb is considered to be a very good specimen. The main predator is the perch, but once a Crucian Carp grows in excess of 1lb it increases its chances of escaping from this enemy. The average weight is ½lb.

The Crucian is very popular with canal anglers and is best caught on summer evenings. Although the usual bait is worms, it can also be caught with floating crusts.

Crucians are sometimes bred on pike farms to feed these hungry predators. They are also very attractive in ornamental pools. However, although their flesh is good they are mostly only eaten in northern and eastern Germany where they are bred commercially in flooded quarries and clay-pits which are unsuitable for common carp and other species. They surpass all other fish in breeding ability due to their high resistance to disease. Exceptional breeding results can be obtained if the water can be kept warm.

MIRROR CARP

This species of the Carp family is to be found mostly in Germany, and exists in lower altitudes. It is distinguishable by the fact that scales cover only some parts of the body in irregular patterns, mostly situated near the head and tail or on the back, but rarely along the lateral line.

It is good eating, but at present is confined mainly to continental hotels and restaurants.

LEATHER CARP

This fish is much like the Tench in its skin texture. It is entirely devoid of scales, and can be identified from the other carp by the number of soft rays: 5-20 in the dorsal and 6-8 in the ventral fin. The lateral line is replaced by a narrow funnel.

104

CARP

Like the Mirror, it is to be found mostly in Germany where its eating qualities are appreciated.

SILVER CARP

A very beautiful fish, originally from China, it is beneficial to most ponds as it clears algae and other water weed. Although its food value is much less than that of the other carp, it costs very little to breed, and it is well worthwhile having a few in your pond to keep it clean. It is sometimes bred purely for ornamentation.

Although the Silver Carp is a large fish, it is also one of the most delicate, and is easily damaged by handling. In the nineteenth century, Sir James Maitland, who bred this species, made his employees wear overalls which were buttoned at the rear so that there was no danger of the carp being damaged when being transferred to other ponds. Fish which are even slightly damaged are liable to develop skin disease and die.

CARP REARING

Carp are one of the easiest fish of all to rear, and once their food value in this country is fully appreciated they will doubtless be a good commercial proposition. They are also inexpensive to rear, and the breeder who invests in a few fingerlings now could well be reaping a very worthwhile harvest in a few years.

A pond, such as the one made by the author and described in Chapter Two, is ideal for Carp of all species. The bottom should be fairly muddy, and there must be ample vegetation.

FEEDING

Sometimes fish are fed with poultry manure but this, although a valuable food, can induce fatal disease, particularly in Silver Carp, if there is any skin damage to the fish.

Boiled potatoes are ideal, provided the price is economical. By far the best food is the artificial variety manufactured to order by Edward Baker Ltd, of Cornard Mills, Sudbury, Suffolk, who supply three types of slow-sinking food. They make it up to order, but it is to be hoped that before long demand will be such that they will be keeping it in stock.

Carp fingerlings should be purchased from a reputable fish-farm. There is very little to do apart from feeding them during their growth, and in their sixth year, when they should have attained a weight of 6lb, they will be ready for eating.

BUILDING UP YOUR MARKET

We, as a nation, are very conservative in our food tastes and, consequently, the breeder will find that without contacts (hotels, restaurants, etc.) he will have a very limited market for his carp. Thus he must be prepared to encourage people to acquire a liking for this fish. Give a few to friends and acquaintances, **but prepare the carp for the table beforehand.** Many people are naturally lazy in the preparation of such food, especially when they have been in the habit of buying from a fishmonger or a frozen-food centre, and they will be reluctant to tackle something when they are not wholly sure if the end product wil be worthwhile.

Public houses are good sources to promote a 'new' food, and the landlord might even experiment with one or two on his 'bar-meals' menu if you provide an initial few free of charge.

Remember that unless you hold a licence to sell fish you could run into trouble if you start selling them to the public for the table.

Carp, in the author's opinion, are going to be a very marketable fish a few years hence. Easily and cheaply bred, the outlay is small, and the rewards could be tremendous.

7

PIKE

THE PIKE

'*Generic Characters.* — Head depressed, large, oblong, blunt; jaws, palatine bones, and vomer, furnished with teeth of various sizes; body elongated, rounded on the back; sides compressed, covered with scales; dorsal fin placed very far back, over the anal fin.'

From: *Britain Fishes.*
William Yarrell.
London, 1836.

Pike (Esox lucius).

CHAPTER SEVEN

Pike

DESCRIPTION

The head of the Pike is large, with powerful jaws and sharp, pointed teeth. The roof of the mouth has small teeth pointing backwards, the cheek is covered with small scales, but only the upper half of the gill cover has large scales. The dorsal fin is flat. There are yellow spots on the sides, and the back is dark to light green. The average life-span is ten years.

The Pike is one of the fastest growing freshwater fishes, and also one of the deadliest predators of small fish. It hunts by daylight, and preys on small fish, ducklings, frogs, mice, and snails, remaining motionless near the banks until its intended prey strays within reach when this deadly hunter strikes quickly.

A Pike swallows a large fish in stages in much the same manner as a boa-constrictor devours its prey. A 4lb fish is capable of satisfying it for up to four days, and during this time it will pass shoals of smaller fish without attacking them.

Pike live in deep holes in the bed or banks of lakes and ponds.

BREEDING

Pike require protection when they are spawning and will often use shallow overgrown ditches. The main enemies of the spawn are ducks and swans which will devour it greedily. Pike spawn towards the end of February, and the eggs hatch very quickly.

Pike are bred mainly for sport. While some people eat them readily, mainly enthusiastic anglers, the flesh is not widely popular. However, lakes need re-stocking with Pike when fished regularly, and it is to this end that the amateur breeder must look. Pike-farms are often small establishments with one or two large pools. As Pike are cannibals, the smaller fish have to be separated from the larger ones.

Deep water is necessary, and pools should have a network of ditches if the Pike are to be encouraged to breed. There must be ample vegetation, and, as an additional precaution, wire-netting covers can be employed to protect the channels from predators such as wild duck.

In the correct lay-out, Pike will breed well. Crucian Carp can be bred in the same water to provide natural food, but the breeder would do well to ensure that there is an abundant supply of snails in the water as well.

The reader who is fortunate enough to have a deep natural pool on his land might do worse than breed Pike in it, even if his main interest is in the rearing of trout or other species in an artificial lay-out. Like Carp, Pike are inexpensive to feed and breed prolifically. Make the best possible use of that old marl pit on your land. A few pounds profit is preferable to having it filled in.

An aura of mystery surrounds the Pike, and there are countless legends of monster fish which inhabit dark unwholesome pools, and which are capable of dragging a man down into the depths! Although a Pike is able to inflict a nasty bite on the careless angler, such stories belong to mythology.

A Killer Pike

Nevertheless, the author cannot suppress a shudder, even today, when he recalls the Pike kept by an old farmer whom he knew many years ago. It is recounted here as yet another

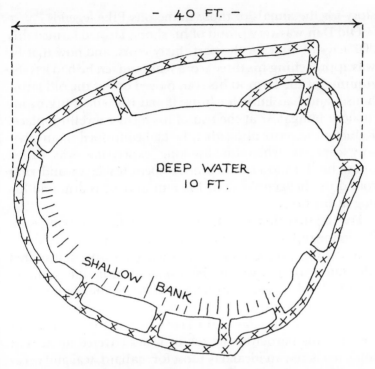

MAIN PIKE POND
LAY-OUT OF ARTIFICIAL DITCHES FOR SPAWNING.
THESE SHOULD BE ALLOWED TO BECOME
OVERGROWN AND SHOULD HAVE WIRE-NETTING
PROTECTION AGAINST PREDATORS.

NURSERY POOL FOR YOUNG FISH.
WIRE-NETTING PROTECTION
OVER ENTIRE SURFACE
IF POSSIBLE.

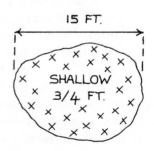

Figure 10 A pike farm.

story for the annals of those numerous Pike legends.

Old Dan was very proud of his shoot. He had farmed this 300 acres of land for the past thirty years, and now that he was approaching his three score years and ten he had left the running of the farm to his son, moved out of the old farmhouse, and had built for himself and his wife a luxurious modern bungalow at the rear of his former dwelling place. Reluctant to retire altogether, he had continued in an advisory capacity when his life-long experience was called upon, but for most of the time he spent his days wandering round the hedgerows with his gun under his arm and his dog at his heels.

For the first time ever Dan began to relax, enjoying each day to the full, and in due course assumed a position akin to that of a full-time gamekeeper, rearing a couple of hundred pheasants for release in the woods during the summer months, and waging constant warfare on the vermin. His favourite place in which to relax and enjoy a well-earned smoke was on the edge of the lake which bordered the main covert. This particular stretch of water covered an area of some ten acres, an ideal day roost for mallard, teal and occasionally Canada geese. Imagine the delight of the old farmer one spring morning when he noticed a mallard swimming on the edge of the reed beds with eight fluffy ducklings in her wake. So thrilled was he at the prospect of a brood being reared within his own domain that he returned to this place of observation day after day, simply for the joy of watching his young charges. All went well for possibly a week and then, one morning, he saw only seven ducklings. He counted them again, thinking his arithmetic must be at fault, but he could in no way account for the discrepancy. Ah well, he sighed, these things happen, and he felt avenged when, later in the day after a long wait, he shot a carrion crow as she returned to her nest in the boughs of a tall oak tree. At least his other ducklings would stand a better chance of survival now.

The following day he only counted six, and then, much to his alarm, on his next visit there were only five following their mother in and out of the dense reeds. Something would have to be done about the diminishing brood before any more losses were incurred. The next day found him back at the lakeside just after daybreak, concealed in some nearby rhododendron bushes, his gun at the ready and his sandwiches and flask at his side. He would spend the whole of the daylight hours here, if necessary, in an attempt to discover and thwart the verminous bird which was preying on these young mallard.

He was very relieved, as the morning wore on, to see five young ducklings swimming only a few yards from his hiding place. Then, as he watched, the last bird in line seemed to disappear slowly beneath the surface of the water. Its four brothers and sisters and its mother seemed quite unaware of what had taken place, only showing signs of alarm when old Dan rushed from the bushes to the edge of the water in an attempt to unravel the mystery which had been troubling him during the last few days.

The water in that particular lake was crystal clear, and from where he stood the old farmer had no difficulty in seeing below the surface to a depth of several feet. He could hardly believe his eyes as the villain was revealed to him for the first time, experiencing the surprise of a cinemagoer who has failed to discover the identity of the murderer in a 'whodunit' before the end of the film. There, possibly a couple of feet below the surface of the water, quite unaware of the disturbance which it had caused, was a pike at least three feet in length. On a sudden impulse Dan raised his gun to his shoulder, and his finger was already on the trigger when a sudden thought crossed his mind. There was a good chance that he would be successful and his shot would eliminate this slaughterer of ducklings, but what if he missed? Suppose the water either deflected the shot, or reduced the power of penetration. Then the killer would be far more

113

wary when next it plundered, and he might never get another chance. There was only one way to be sure. . . .

For the remainder of that day Dan sat on the shore of the lake, his fishing rod in his hands, and his pipe clenched firmly between his teeth. As bait he was using a dead sparrow, for obviously this particular fish had a liking for feathered food. His rod, made of carefully chosen East Indian bamboo and about 12 feet in length, was ideal for the task on which he was engaged. He felt sure that this particular fish must weigh somewhere in the region of 25lb. He remained there until dusk finally fell and then, somewhat disappointed, he trudged homewards, feeling that his efforts had all been to no avail.

The next day found him back at the water's edge shortly after dawn had broken. Again he was using a sparrow as his bait, his one consolation for his previous lack of success being the thought that perhaps this monster fish restricted itself to a diet of one bird per day!

Shortly after mid-day there was a tug on his line, and then the fight was on. The water threshed and foamed as the pike fought for its very life. Old Dan hung on grimly and, as the battle raged, he wondered from time to time whether he was ever going to be able to land his foe. However, his determination was his greatest ally, and twenty minutes later the piratical fish lay upon the bank at his feet. He had won, but he wasn't finished yet. He had brought with him especially for the purpose a large polythene bag, inside of which there was a wet sack, and into this went the pike for its short journey back to the farm. Dan had some very special plans in store for him.

At the rear of the rickyard, sunk into the ground to a depth of six feet, was a rectangular resevoir, some eight feet long by five feet wide, used specifically for supplying the cattle with drinking water during times of drought. Into this went the killer from the lake, this water wolf who would terrorise young ducklings no more.

The author remembers seeing this particular pike one day in his early boyhood, when he accompanied his parents on a visit to the farm in question. So fearsome a prospect did it present in the depths of its artificial home, that he stepped back from the brink in awe, and no amount of coaxing would induce him to venture back for another peep.

That was the only time he ever saw that giant fish, but years later it was old Dan's son who told him the full story. Twice daily his father would feed his 'pet', and this continued for almost two years. However, during the second winter of the pike's confinement, Dan suffered a severe bout of influenza, and whilst he was incapacitated, rather than tend to the fearsome prisoner, his two sons caught it again, cooked it, and attempted to eat it. Alas, not only was the flavour unpalatable, they claimed, but the pike itself, which must have attained a fair age, was so tough as to render it virtually inedible. Consequently, the remains of the terror of the lake finished up in the dustbin, much to the old farmer's dismay when he was up and about again. His only consolation was that any duck which bred on the lake in future could do so without fearing the ravages of this monster from the depths.

Surely these sons had no knowledge of the preparation and cooking of Pike, for coarse as this fish is, it can be rendered extremely palatable with a little forethought.

8
GOLDFISH

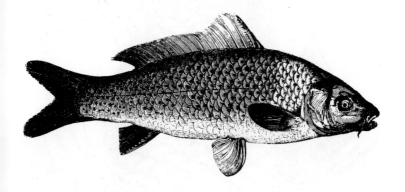

Common Carp (Cyprinus carpio).

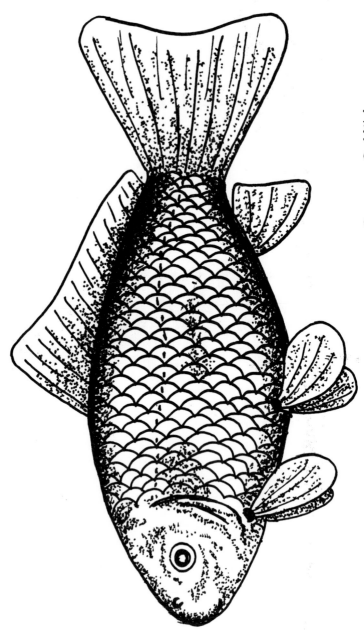

Common Goldfish   Frank W. Orme

CHAPTER EIGHT

Goldfish

HISTORY

The breed of Goldfish with which we are familiar today was created by the Chinese through inter-breeding of several varieties. It is supposedly a multi-hued relative of the Common Carp, a belief which has existed ever since its introduction to Europe, but this is refuted by Frank W. Orme in his book *Fancy Goldfish Culture* (Saiga Publishing). He claims that it is a distinct species and is not descended from the Crucian Carp, and neither is it a sport of the Common Carp which, unlike the Goldfish, has barbels at the corner of its mouth.

The Goldfish was first mentioned during China's Sung Dynasty (AD 960-1279), but by the sixteenth century the Chinese were involved in selective breeding. Then, in the eighteenth century, new trade routes took the Goldfish to Europe, and King Louis XV of France obtained some of the first specimens as a present for Madame de Pompadour.

By the nineteenth century this fish had reached the New World and was being sold in New York in 1865. Nowadays, an average of 60 million common Goldfish are bought annually in the United States of America.

BREEDING

The common Goldfish averages six or eight saleable offspring for every 100 eggs laid by the female. This low figure is a result of the fish being a cannibal, and greedily devouring its own eggs.

119

The Goldfish is extremely hardy. We have proof of this in their ability to survive in sealed plastic bags, and many are offered as prizes at fairgrounds in this type of container. Indeed, some are even exported in this manner.

The size of a Goldfish is determined by the tank in which it is kept, and the amount of food it receives. Ideally, they should be kept in a pond such as the one described by the author in Chapter Two. In this environment they will grow to a greater size than their counterparts in the small household bowl or tank, or even the indoor aquarium.

A word of warning, however, to the breeder who decides to keep his fish in an outdoor pond. They must be safeguarded against predators. Cats are the main enemies, and next-door's tabby will hardly be able to believe his luck if you present him with a number of fish which he has only to flip out of the water with his paw! In rural areas it is not improbable that a passing heron will discover the pond, and if this happens every fish will disappear with great rapidity in a single raid.

Perhaps one of the least known enemies of the Goldfish is the frog. The breeder who welcomes these creatures in his garden must take steps to keep them away from his Goldfish, for a single frog is capable of devouring half-a-dozen in a day. Wire-netting is the answer, even if it does spoil the ornamental appearance of the pond, but this protective covering need not be a permanent fixture. A moveable frame is best, one that can be removed during those fine weekends and evenings when the reader relaxes in his garden and admires his fish. It can be replaced in a few seconds to guard them during his absence.

However, Goldfish grow to a greater size out of doors in a roomy pond, but they must be bred indoors in a larger aquarium than the conventional bowl so common in many homes.

On a commercial basis the Japanese and Koreans are among the most successful Goldfish breeders in the world, but for sheer volume of output we must credit the Americans, who market these fish by the ton.

In the United States of America, Goldfish are housed in large concrete ponds on these specialist farms. They are fed on a composite of soyabeans, wheat, meat, fish-meal and vitamins. Apart from the common Goldfish, they breed other varieties such as Fantails, Moors, Calicoes, and Shubunkins.

Seldom can Goldfish be sexed except at the approach of the breeding season when the males develop a surface on each gill-cover similar to emery-paper. The eggs are collected from the females on mats, and taken to a nursery pond where there are no adult fish to eat them. The male chromosomes in each egg join into a single unit with the female, then split up again, and finally hatch out after five or six days. They are then transferred from the aquarium into a spacious pond where they grow to about an inch in a month. The young fish are black in colour for the first three or four months.

Of course, the amateur breeder will operate on a more modest scale. **He must bear in mind that each Goldfish requires eight pints of water for every inch of its length**. At the start of the spawning season he must observe his fish closely, and remove the eggs to a separate tank as soon as possible after they have been spawned. Goldfish mate at night and spawn on the following morning. The female generally lays about 1,000 eggs. Soon after hatching the young fish must be transferred to a larger tank, and within a week or so they will be ready for the pond in the garden.

Food is obtainable at most reputable aquarium shops. As a guide to the prospective buyer, this should contain a minimum of 30% Crude Protein, 10% Crude Fibre, and 3% Crude Fat. The basic ingredients are fish meal, oat gruel, soyabean meal, torula dried yeast, potato powder, cod liver, kelp and Dayfly eggs.

Goldfish should be fed two or three times a day. **Care must be taken that they are not overfed, for a surplus of food fouls the water, especially in hot weather, and when this happens the fish will die in a matter of hours.**

Goldfish are possibly the easiest of all fish to market. Pet-shops will often be glad of a regular supply, but in many cases sales direct to the public will follow an advertisement or two. The reader will find, in all probability, that demand exceeds supply.

DISEASES

There are three ways in which diseases can be conveyed to your fish:

1   By the introduction of new fish to the pool or tank.
2   From plant life.
3   From live foods obtained from water in which other fish live.

In order to ascertain the health of your fish, they should be held in the hand and turned on their sides in the water. If the eyes roll so that the pupil cannot be seen, then the gold-fish is in good health. If the pupil is visible, then the fish is suffering from some ailment.

Red spots on the skin generally mean that there is some bacterial ailment. Eye infections are diagnosed by an enlargement of the eye or a greyish cataract. Abnormal swell-ings or a thin hollow-bellied appearance may be due to inter-nal disorders. An early diagnosis generally means that the ailment can be cured. A neglected fish usually dies.

Ailing fish should be put in a separate tank and observed frequently, but the temperature in the 'isolation' tank must be the same as the one from which the goldfish has been removed. The fish must be handled gently, and those from which it has been removed watched closely in case they show signs of sickness also.

Possibly the most comprehensive work available today on

goldfish breeding is *Fancy Goldfish Culture* by Frank W. Orme. In this book the author deals at length with diseases and their cure, and the beginner is advised to study this.

DANGERS OF LEAPING GOLDFISH

One final word of warning to the amateur Goldfish breeder. **Goldfish are capable of leaping out of the water to a height of several inches, and there is always the danger that if the level of the water is near the top of the tank they will jump out altogether.**

The author kept one such fish that leapt out of a tank on three occasions, in spite of continued reduction in water level in an attempt to combat this. The first time it happened, the Goldfish was discovered missing from its tank one morning when the members of the family came down to breakfast. A search was made and the missing fish was discovered beneath a sideboard, covered in hairs shed by a moulting yellow labrador! The writer had faint hopes for his Goldfish's survival, but immediately returned it to the water. It alternated between spending intervals floating on the top and resting on the bottom, but within a week it was back to normal.

On the second occasion it landed on the table, and its plight was detected when it was heard flapping about. This time it was on dry land only a few minutes, and suffered no ill-effects whatsoever.

However, this particular fish tempted Fate once too often, and its final escape from its home proved fatal, for it happened during the nocturnal hours, and was found to be dead when the members of the household came downstairs next morning. As further proof of the hardiness of this particular fish, it, too, was a 'fairground specimen' which came in a plastic bag!

In the light of these experiences the author places a sheet of gauze over the tank upon retiring at night or leaving the house in the daytime.

123

WATER

Goldfish, unlike many other species, survive well in tap-water. Only in recent months, however, has the author been fully aware of the difference between water from a tap in an urban area and that piped from a spring-fed reservoir. In his former home, the writer used to change the water in the Goldfish tank every few days as it became cloudy. However, in new surroundings, where the water has been tested and found to be the purest in the district, the only indication that the tank-water needs changing is when the stones in the bottom become covered with a type of green fungus. This never happened when chlorinated water was used, yet no difference was detected in the general health of the fish.

The late Sir Winston Churchill was a Goldfish enthusiast, and had several ponds built at Chartwell in order to pursue his hobby.

Possibly the most famous Goldfish of all was Oscar, a World War II mascot, which was kept in a steel helmet full of water. It can be argued whether or not this was preferable to the claustrophobic plastic bags!

The Goldfish is bred purely as an ornamental fish, and in no way can it be listed amongst the edible varieties. Yet, with 25 million kept in British homes, the enthusiastic rearer is assured of their popularity.

9
VARIOUS FRESHWATER FISH

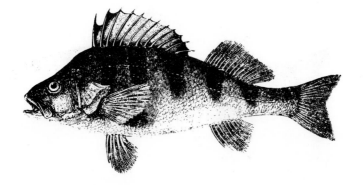

Perch (Perca fluviatilis).

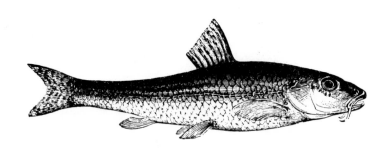

Gudgeon (Gobio fluviatilis).

CHAPTER NINE

Various Freshwater Fish

GOLDEN ORF'E

The Golden Orf'e is mainly an ornamental fish, very similar to the Bream, although it is eaten in Germany as is the Carp. Usually it is kept in park lakes or large ponds, but is also found naturally in rivers.

This fish has a small blunt head with a cleft mouth, and small scales in regular rows. The lateral line is parallel with the belly line. The dorsal fin has 3 hard and 8 or 9 soft rays, the pectoral fin one hard and 15-16 soft, the abdominal fin 3 hard and 8 soft, and the concave and anal fins have 3 hard and 9-11 soft. The forked caudal fin has 19 soft rays. The lateral line comprises 56-61 scales. In colour the Golden Orf'e is a greyish or blackish blue, with silvery flanks, and a white or greyish belly.

Breeding

Those who are contemplating breeding this fish need to have a pool of deep, *clean* water.

The Golden Orf'e spawns during April and May, the female laying about 100,000 eggs on the roots of water weed beneath overgrown banks. An adult specimen attains an average weight of 1lb and a length of 12-16 inches, and there are records in Finland of one reaching an age of 14 years.

The market, however, will be limited, and sales can only be expected to those owning gardens with ornamental pools.

PERCH

The Perch is a very beautiful freshwater fish with brilliant, scintillating colours. The upper part of the body is a rich greenish-brown, the lower regions a yellowish white. There are five to seven dark transverse bands on the sides, with golden irides. The first dorsal fin is brown, and the membrane connecting two or three of the first and last rays have black spots. The second dorsal fin and the pectoral fins are pale brown, the ventral, anal and caudal fins bright vermilion. The teeth are small, and curving backwards inside the mouth is a transverse palatine membrane.

Breeding

The reader first needs to find the spawn. It takes the form of long ribbon-like folds and is to be located in quiet streams or backwaters on the roots of trees which protrude into the water. It is a favourite food of both swans and ducks. The spawning season is at the end of April and the beginning of May.

This spawn should be taken back to a pool where it needs to be protected from its enemies for at least two weeks. Once the young fish hatch out they are reasonably safe because Pike avoid Perch on account of their spikes.

In the right kind of pool, one with ample undergrowth and water weed, Perch will look after themselves and grow quickly, the average weight being 3lb.

Often it is harder to reduce the number of Perch in a pool than it is to breed them. If too many small Perch are being caught in a pool then it is a sure sign that it is over-stocked, and the only remedy is to net as many as possible and take them to another stretch of water. They are hardy, and are able to live for several hours out of water.

Perch are bred for both sport and food. Often they are the first catch of a young angler for they are fairly easily caught. The average weight of a mature specimen is 3lb, and the firm white flesh is extremely palatable although it is not

128

often eaten outside angling circles. Nevertheless, the breeder should be able to sell his Perch for re-stocking angling waters.

The Pikeperch is the most widely spread predatory fish next to the Pike, and is to be found in lakes with gravelly bottoms and *clean* rivers. Originally it came to Central Europe after the end of the Ice Age.

The body is symmetrical, variegated in colour, with a narrow head and a large mouth. The flanks have 8-12 brownish black bands, and there are black spots between the spines of the anterior dorsal fin in 10 irregular rows, and these are also to be found between the rays of the posterior dorsal fin. The belly of the female is pure white during the spawning season whilst that of the male is marbled blue. The two dorsal fins are separated by a narrow gap. The anterior dorsal fin has 13-17 hard spines, the posterior 1-3 hard and 19-27 soft rays. The lateral line has 80-97 scales. The mouth has innumerable small and several larger tapered teeth.

Breeding

Much of that written on the Pike in Chapter Seven applies to the Pikeperch. The breeder needs a deep pool with a sand or gravel base.

Pikeperch spawn in the spring in pairs. The female lays 100,000-300,000 eggs, 1.5mm in diameter, on sand, gravel or the roots of weeds in the bottom of the pool. The male guards them fiercely whilst they are hatching.

The young hatch within a fortnight, and by their third year they will have grown to 12-20 inches, weighing 1-3lb. The maximum size they will attain is 3½-4½ feet, and a weight of 25-30lb. The young feed on plankton at first, but later become predatory and prey on small fish, hunting during the evening.

The Pikeperch is very popular with anglers, and is one of

the most valuable of predatory fishes. The breeder will no doubt be able to market them for the re-stocking of pools, but although they are good eating they are not widely popular. Again, this is a limited market.

CHAR

The Char is a salmonoid fish which lives in both salt and freshwater in Europe. Similar in appearance to the trout, it is easily distinguished by the mouth structure. Whilst the vomerine bone in the centre of the trout's mouth has teeth all along it, the Char has only a few at the front of the bone.

There are 130-140 small scales in the lateral line. The dorsal fin has 3 or 4 hard and 8-11 soft rays, the anal fin 3 or 4 hard and 7 or 8 soft. The first branchial arch has 18-30 gill-rakers. The mouth is deeply cleft. The general colouring is rich; in the spawning season the back is blue, the flanks greenish-blue and covered with small red or orange spots, the belly is bright red, and the area directly beneath the mouth is vivid yellow. The front edge of the pectoral fins, ventral fins and anal fin is white, whilst the dorsal and caudal fins are the same colour as the back. Apart from the spawning season, the colouring generally is paler, the belly being silver.

Breeding

The Char is a cold water migratory fish, attaining a length of up to 3½ feet with a weight of 32lb. The quality of its flesh is comparable with that of the Sea Trout, and it is of great sporting value.

The author would refer readers to Chapter Five on salmon. Char can be bred in an identical manner, but the breeder must have access to an estuary river in order to be successful. Often Char are reared alongside Salmon and Sea Trout.

GRAYLING

The Grayling is a freshwater member of the salmon family. It has a long high dorsal fin with a convex dorsal edge and black stripes from front to rear. Unlike the salmon, the tail fin is forked. In colour this fish is greyish-green on the back, the scales are small and silver, and the flanks are silver with black spots.

Breeding

Grayling spawn between March and May, the ova hatching out in about a fortnight, but care must be taken not to let the temperature of the water in the tanks rise above 48°F as if this happens fungoid growth develops quickly and the whole of the spawn can be killed in this way in a very short time. **The fry, although small, are hardy, but the mature fish are delicate and die very easily if care is not taken when transporting them.**

The female lays 3,000-5,000 eggs per pound of her weight, the ova hatching in about three weeks, and the young fish spend most of their time under the protective cover of weeds.

In the early stages they feed on insects, larvae and spawn of other fishes, but towards maturity they become predatory. The males mature in their third year, the females in their fourth. At the end of their first summer the young fish are 4 inches long and weigh about an ounce, progressing to about 1lb in the fourth year. Even in the severest winter the Grayling will continue to feed.

Rearing

As for trout, using a lay-out of ponds fed by running water.

GUDGEON

This is a river fish preferring sandy or gravel bottoms where it breeds prolifically.

The head is flat and elongated. The back is greyish-green

131

to gold with black or brown spots, the belly is silver, and the fins are yellow with brown flecks. It is similar to the Barbel in shape. The lower jaw is broad, the tail deeply forked, and the outer rays are almost as long again as the centre ones with about 10 rows of scales. The gill-covers are light green, and the ventral and anal fins are almost white, being tinged with brown. The dorsal fin and tail are pale brown but spotted with darker brown.

Breeding

Gudgeon spawn in May, and at this time the male develops tubercles on the head. They spawn in shoals, the females laying their eggs on stones and weeds in gravelly shallows. After hatching, the fry remain in large shoals, feeding on algae, progressing to insects.

Gudgeon are much preyed upon, their chief enemies being Pike and Perch.

They are good food value, and are also popular with inexperienced anglers because these fish so often move in shoals. During the eighteenth and nineteenth century 'Gudgeon Parties' were held on the River Thames, a sporting and social occasion in which the anglers and their guests feasted on their catch.

Yet the commercial value of this fish is very limited, and whilst it is possible to collect the spawn and hatch them in a pool for later release in rivers, the breeder would do better devoting his time to a more saleable species.

BLEAK

The Bleak lives in both still and running water. The dorsal fin has 3-4 hard, and 7-9 soft rays, the anal fin 3 hard and 15-19 soft. The lateral line comprises 42-52 scales. The mouth is turned upwards, the eyes are large, and the scales are silvery.

Plate 11 Golden Tench (From painting by Jim Dunford.)

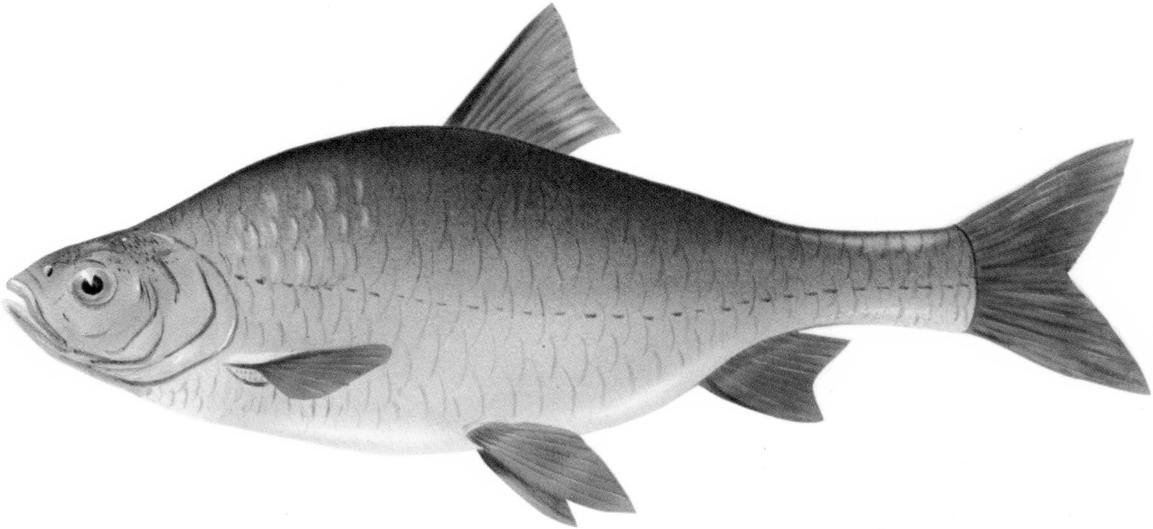

Plate 12 Golden Rudd *(From painting by Jim Dunford.)*

Breeding

The Bleak spawns in April and May, depositing its eggs on stones or weeds. Its favourite food is zooplankton, but it also feeds on insects. A mature fish attains a length of 6-8 inches and weighs about 1lb.

Commercial Value

The Bleak, which is not found in either Scotland or Ireland, is of commercial importance because 'Essence d'Orient' (pearl essence) is obtained from its scales and is used in the manufacture of artificial pearls.

A worthy quarry, it is a challenge to any angler.

TENCH

The Brown/Green and also the Golden Tench is bred for both ornamentation and sport, as well as being prized for its food value in Germany where baked Tench is regarded as a delicacy.

The head is large and blunt, and the mouth is small with a minute barbule at each corner. The lips are flesh-coloured, the tongue is short, the irides golden yellow, the eyes are small, and the body is covered with small scales, about 48 in all, in an oblique row between the base of the dorsal fin and the origin of the ventral fin. The overall colour is greenish-olive gold, with dark brown fins and light underparts.

The Tench is a member of the Carp family, and is usually found in sluggish rivers, as well as in lakes and ponds where it remains mostly in dense weed in the shallows. In deep pools it is rarely seen as it shuns strong light and remains in deep water. It is basically a scavenger, but its acute senses enable it to hunt for food in pitch darkness. A mature fish ranges from 1½-4lb in weight.

Breeding

The Tench hibernates during winter, and spawns in June-July when the female lays about 275,000 eggs. After hatching, the fry hide amidst thick weed in an attempt to escape from predators. A gregarious fish, the Tench remains in shoals all its life. The average life span is from 10-30 years.

The Tench is capable of surviving in mud for several weeks when a pond dries up as its body is covered with mucus which prevents the skin from drying out, and the gill filaments are divided so that they utilise oxygen fully.

Tench Farming

Tench are farmed on a commercial basis, but the reader with a sizeable pond at his disposal will also be able to breed them successfully. Fish farmers are able to obtain a threefold increase on the average weight of a wild Tench. Females generally put on 30% more weight than males.

In Germany the Tench was probably reared for the table before the Carp became popular. **It is very easily bred in ponds, and can be ideally reared along with Carp.**

Tench are more thorough feeders than Carp, burrowing deep into the mud at the bottom of the pool in search of food. The best ratio for the rearer is one Tench to ten Carp, and more of the former are inclined to have adverse effects on the latter.

Tench are also useful in cultivating a marketable protein crop from ponds which are too overgrown and unsuitable to breed Carp, but they can be time-wasting due to their liking for lying in the mud which makes them difficult to catch.

Unfortunately, Tench are not popular on the menu in this country, and therefore the amateur fish farmer will have to rely mainly upon sales for ornamental purposes. There is a fair demand for small specimens by owners of aquariums.

The usual bait for catching Tench is bread or worms, but they are best caught with a moving bait on account of their poor eyesight, the rippling of the water attracting them when otherwise they would not see the bait.

134

GOLDEN RUDD

The Golden Rudd is similar in appearance to the Roach. The dorsal fin is close to the tail, and the iris is a light orange. The teeth are arranged in two rows, the front row having five large on each bone, the second only three. The pectoral and caudal fins are scarlet, the dorsal grey. The dorsal fin has 2 or 3 hard, and 8 or 9 soft rays, and the anal fin has 3 hard and 9-12 soft. The lateral line comprises 38-42 scales.

The Golden Rudd feeds mostly on vegetable food, and is usually found in shoals in the lower reaches of a sluggish river. It does not like swift currents.

Breeding

The Golden Rudd spawns in April or May, the female laying 80,000-100,000 eggs on plants. These eggs hatch out in about a fortnight, and the young feed on zooplankton in the early stages. Once they have attained a length of 3 inches they begin to feed on plants, and on reaching maturity their diet is soft water plants and algae. An average adult Golden Rudd attains a length of 10-12 inches with a maximum weight of up to 4lb.

Rearing

The rearer with a quiet overgrown backwater should be successful in breeding Golden Rudd. Natural plant life is essential, and the fish will breed and look after themselves, so long as they are protected from predators. They are the staple food of predatory game fish and may be purchased by anglers and clubs renting stretches of river. They have a sporting value of their own, even though their flesh is not very palatable. In some instances they may be purchased to stock ornamental streams in extensive grounds.

CISCO

The Cisco is a lake-inhabiting member of the salmon family, easily recognisable by its large scales and silvery body which is darker on the back. The eggs are smaller than those of either trout or salmon. This fish shuns bright daylight, preferring deep clean water.

The reader with a small lake on his land may benefit from introducing a few fingerlings and allowing them to breed purely for his own sporting pleasure, but there is very little demand for them commercially.

The Eel has a snake-like body, the vertebral column containing 110-119 vertebrae. The head is small and pointed, although the female has a wider head than the male. The body is covered with very small scales. Its powerful jaws have tapered teeth, but the mouth itself is small with large lips. The skin is thick and slimy. There are no ventral fins. The gill-slits are situated in the immediate vicinity of the pectoral fins which have 15-29 soft rays and are the only paired fins of the Eel. The anal fin has 176-249 soft rays, and the caudal fin has 7-12 soft rays. On its journey down river to the sea the colour of the Eel becomes silvery.

Rearing

The Eel is of considerable commercial importance owing to its palatable flesh, but Taiwan is the only country to date to produce Eels in any real quantity. There are two main species of Eel, the Japanese and the European.

Eel-farming is also increasing rapidly in Thailand, Malaysia, Vietnam, Indonesia and the Philippines, but with varied success. In 1975 the first Eel farm was established in Cuba, near Havana.

The most important thing which the prospective breeder must bear in mind is that Eels need well-oxygenated water (see chapter on equipment p. 49). The water must be free from all pollution, and temperature must be maintained around 12°C. If the temperature falls below this, then feed-

ing and growing will halt, and the Eels will in all probability die in a very short time.

Eels are best bred in a large aquarium or indoor pool
which meets the requirements already stated, and the amateur will have to work on a small scale in the early stages,
expanding slowly.

Feeding

Eel food in meal form is obtainable from Messrs. Edward
Baker Ltd, of Cornard Mills, Sudbury, Suffolk.

STICKLEBACK

The Stickleback seldom exceeds 3 inches in length. Small
teeth form a narrow band in each jaw, but there are none on
the vomer, palatine bones or tongue. The gill-opening is
large. The principal dorsal spine is long and blunt, its
lateral serrations small and few in number. A membrane is
attached to the spine by which it is depressed. The ventral
spine is triangular at the base, and the serrations on the
upper edge are large and not thickly set, whilst those on the
lower edge are small and numerous. The whole length of
the sides are protected by a series of elongated bone plates
which are arranged vertically. A small fold of skin forms a
horizontal crest on each side of the tail. The males are distinguished by their pink under-surface, but both sexes are at
their most brilliant during the spawning season. The back
is green, and the belly, sides, and cheeks are silvery.

The Stickleback lives in both salt and fresh water. It feeds
on worms, insects, and the fry of smaller fish, and is naturally ferocious. These fish regularly battle amongst themselves using their spines with deadly effect.

Breeding

The Stickleback spawns during the summer months, and
the reader who contemplates breeding them needs a large
pool with plenty of plant life in it. It would be inadvisable

to keep them with any other species due to their pugnacious temperament.

Some years ago attempts were made to obtain oil from them, but nowadays they are used as a base for certain fertilizers, and for laboratory research. In order to obtain a regular market and subsequent profitability, the breeder needs first to gain experience with Stickleback and then to rear them in quantity. They breed easily, needing very little attention, but in order to reap good returns they need to be marketed in bulk.

Some Brief Notes on General Fish Breeding

There is no maximum depth of water for a fish pond in the garden, but it should not be less than twelve inches. It is unlikely that the pond will freeze whilst an aerator is working, but in the case of a pond which does not have this type of equipment do not break holes in the ice. Fish can survive beneath ice for reasonable periods. If, however, you anticipate a long severe spell, the fish should be removed to another pond, preferably one with an aerator.

Both Carp and Trout can be kept in the same pool as Goldfish without detriment. Thirty Trout and twenty Carp can survive comfortably in a pond with a 12ft diameter and a depth of 12 inches.

Carp and Trout can be fed on household table scraps in the event of the breeder running out of food. Trout will eat minced meat, and Carp like flaked maize and ground barley.

The cost in producing each pound of edible fish will depend on individual factors such as the cost of commercial food and whether an aerator is operated continually. One thing is certain, though: **considerable savings will be made over fish purchased from a fishmonger.**

INDEX